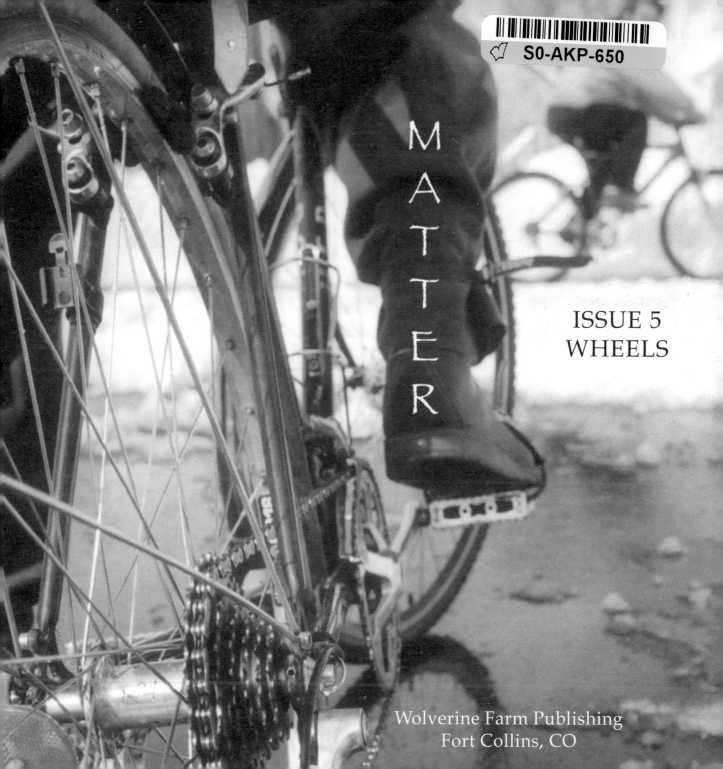

MATTER

ISSUE 5
WHEELS

Wolverine Farm Publishing
Fort Collins, CO

Did you turn in your sleep last night?

LCCN: 2004-214172
ISBN: 0-9741999-2-3
ISSN: 1548-8411
(an I 4 an I 4 an ISBN)

Average kcal/km per person:
Bicycle & 1 Rider (15mph): 25
Walker (4mph): 50
Runner (10 mph): 75
Train & Riders (30mph): 110
Car & 5 Riders (60mph): 190
Car & 1 Rider (60mph): 810

"You can never become one with the universe by collecting records," or so purports Paul Trembath, who I fear has left me standing in an articulate state. But as I say later, which is really me echoing someone earlier, it's a nomad nomad world, so what else can we do but move forward, with or without constructs, which we are biologically prepared to do, considering our skeletal structure and the way our eyes are positioned? If nature intended us to be looking over our shoulder constantly, we would not be fashioned the way we are. So bless your evolution to date. I write this from the new Matter House. Ad got the shitty room and for that I am sorry. Poe got the best room and she pays for it, everyday. In the garage are no less than nine bicycles (with a red one parked out front, locked to itself in the rain), and we don't even flinch at this fact. This issue was going to be the bicycle issue and even though that idea got lampooned in an early triangulation meeting, we still feel like we paid some homage to the most glorious invention ever between our legs. But you will ultimately have to decide things for yourself, but you can always trust this: if you pull up to the Matter House on a bicycle, you will be admitted as friend. We will lube your chain, feed you what meager food we may have, give you something warm and soothing to drink, and wish you the best of luck with things. We would offer you a warm place to sleep, but that really is asking too much. For that we would have to chop down the trees that surround this entire house, thereby allowing sunlight. But we will not chop down the trees, at least not for firewood. As it is now, this place is very much a meat locker, which we joke about quite a bit. Much like we joke about a fifth of five, referring to the portion of women's words included here in. Poe is hoping to address that it the weeklies around town; a problem of "the distribution of submissions," as she calls it. Blundering as we did in our failure to include enough females or pertinent information about windmills and wind farms, we hope to correct ourselves futurely. Don't fret! We will continue trying, over and over and over, conveniently like a wheel, as we hope you will. "Organize, simplify, purify," one of us says. Get a bike and ride it, and pay cash for things you buy. It's easier that way.

Matter spun by:
Wolverine Farm Publishing
PO BOX 814 Fort Collins, CO 80522
www.matterjournal.com

W.F.P.

G.R.O.W.L.

:yb nups rettaM
gnihsilbuP mraF enirevloW
22508 OC ,snilloC troF 418 XOB OP
moc.lanruojrettam.www

WETURNYOUCANWETURNYOUCANWETURNYOUCANWETURNYOUCANW

can we turn

n we turn you

turn

can we urn you

can we turn you

cany

we turn you

can we

Publisher/Editor: *Todd Simmons.*
Co-Editor: *Erin Morrill.*
Visual Editor/Graphic Design: *Adam Garry.*
Nonfiction Editor: *Gary Wockner.*
Contributing Editors: *Trevor Harwood.*
Evan P. Schneider.

literature art movement literature art movement litera

"But as I say, I read it at a gulp without screwing my wits tight to the a

Tulessein K. Shulder. Lust for Velocity 07
Derrick Esposito. Uninventing the Wheel 08
Kendra Kellogg. Belmont Stop 14
Blair Oliver. Eldorado 16
Brian Kiteley. Song of North Hampton 26
Clotilde Wright. Neighborhood Vignettes 31
William deRosset. Brevet Ride 32
Alex Paozols. Thunder 35
Genevieve Betts. Swallowing Stone 43
Steven Church. Unpublished Letter to the Editor 46
Jacob Burd. Life in France 49
Wayne Sheldrake. Hillclimb 54
Jefferson Navicky. Snow 60
Morgan Reitmeyer. Cycles of the Heart 61
Trevor Even. Eleven Dollar Minimum 65

wolverine farm publishing

71 Pathway of the Waves *Heather Martin.*
75 Livre Melancholique *David Gruber.*
80 Bicycle: The History
81 Review *Evan P. Schneider.*
84 Excerpt
86 Interview with author David Herlihy
90 The Most Irrational *Patrick Odenbeck.*
93 Prophetic State *Keith Kimmel.*
94 Introduction to Cultural Anthropology
(limited stops) *Gary Norris.*
98 Animal Intelligence *Bin Ramke.*
101 What Goes Up *Derrick Jensen.*

art movement literature art movement literature art m
ment. This is a method I find very profitable: then go back and screw."

virginia woolf

Journals, 20 April 1935

Matt Roberts: The Fonz 116
Dick Diamond & Harriet Welch. A Conversation 119
Laura Mullen. Dedicated (Dictated) 123
Robert Urqubart. Returning Dust to Stone 125
Joan Marsan. Clastic 133
Todd Simmons. Its a Nomad, Nomad World 134
Sue Ring deRosset. America, Roaring 140
Gary Wockner. Hideaway 143
Carol Deering. Somewhere West of Laramie 148
Erin Morrill. Pave 149
Claire Petersky. Get Off the Fucking Road 152
Ian Tyson. Disco Poems: Four to the Floor 153
Cyclographies 175

issue 5: wheels

Photo & Illustration Credits

1904 COLOMBIA #128 FIXED GEAR ROADSTER

1907 J.W. GRADY NEW ENGLAND SPECIAL RACER

1980 LIBERTAS 2 SPEED

hanalia, do you have a button presser? a library
anih/English Dictionary, condoms, Three sorts of
 cash som we don;t leave a trail,, assorted music
to lure women, such as harmonicas,guitars, and ra
er, a collage of od stickers, a pair of binoculars
eral propaganda, frisbee, drums, kites, Tim Steele
e, desire, adventure, glue, riff-raff, a 1930 atla
ons of mass lovestruction, a bouquet of sporting e
 myths, and themes, backbones, spines, and snails
anical nosed, extra rope, jumper cabels, a cinder
ich of deception, a monkey on my back, a peice of
ings of Milarepa, some honest thoughts inspired m
 of idleness, Intensity, my knack to find other a
dipity, circles and squares, ideas on topical cre
, quick wit, a telemarketers precistence, a hippo
tion, maybe an article for Matter, a super heroes
corder, number-sense, a warm hat (don;t leave hom
reen, seeds of change, lyrics undiscovered, prose
 lighter), **lust and a touch of American arrogance**
, a peice of wheat found in a crop circle, a maga
mation on literature, background information on A
stick, a gamblers spirit, a leatherman, -I will n
ter-egos, pain medication, stupidity, carelessnes

Uninventing the Wheel

Dereke Esposito

"Those who are inspired by a model other than Nature, a mistress above all masters, are laboring in vain."
—Leonardo da Vinci

Technology is hailed as one of the qualities that separates humans from nature. One can look to the many technological breakthroughs that have occurred over the course of *Homo sapiens'* rise to dominance on this Earth as evidence of human superiority over all other creatures: vessels able to sail the ocean seas, sport-utility vehicles that can handle most any terrain, and airplanes ready to whisk passengers into outer space. However, as human consciousness begins to grasp that diminishing natural resources affect us along with the rest of creation, from the amoebas to the zebras—that we're all in this big petri dish together—people are beginning to look for alternatives. But what alternatives are there?

Fortunately, one need not travel to distant galaxies to find an example of an alternative technology. With a sense of wonder, stare in awe at how trees are able to transport gallons of water up hundreds of feet, in silence. Spiders weave webs out of silk that is pound-for-pound stronger than steel, without the use of toxic chemicals. Hummingbirds routinely cross the Gulf of Mexico on the energy acquired from a teaspoon of nectar. Luckily, we have an example of sustainability already in place. Nature has been tweaking technology for 3.7 billion years.

Uninventing the Wheel

So where does human technology diverge from that found in nature? The wheel sits at the core of human ingenuity. Wheels literally carry our land vehicles; they turn our ships' propellers, aircraft rotary turbines, snow blowers, trench diggers, and conveyor belts. Our crankshafts, rotary electric motors, rotating pulleys, gears, capstans, hinges, cams, windlasses, ratchet wheels, roller bearings, and spindles all rely upon the wheel. The wheel, as evidenced by its pervasiveness in human technology, has proven to be an extraordinarily efficient mechanism. So, where is the wheel used in nature? As my *Introduction to Biology* textbook stated, "Nature has never invented the wheel," yet that's not entirely true. Besides humans, the one example of nature's use of the wheel is that of the primitive bacterial flagellum, discovered by Howard Berg and associates in the 1970's. The flagellum is a swimming device found in some bacteria that uses three parts to enable locomotion—a paddle, a rotor, and a motor. The internal motor turns the rotor (wheel) which in turn rotates the paddle, creating movement.

The biologist Steven Vogel, in his book *Cats' Paws and Catapults*, states that "we do wonders with wheels and rotary motion; nature makes fully competent boats, aircraft, and terrestrial vehicles that lack them entirely." Instead of using a wheel for efficient movement over flat surfaces, nature employs legs with energy-saving tendons that are able to maneuver over uneven terrain. Where human designs rely upon ball-bearings for near frictionless joints, nature chooses cartilage surrounded by synovial fluid.

In addition to a lack of the wheel and its manifestations, nature diverges from human designs in other important ways:

- Nature uses benign manufacturing, assembling materials at body temperature, with low pressure, and non-toxic chemicals. The majority of human industrial processes involve the use of large amounts of heat, high pressures, and toxic chemicals (heat, beat, and treat) that are extracting huge tolls on the environment.

- Nature grows its crops as perennial polycultures, supporting diversity and redundancy Humans grow annual monocultures, in need of massive amounts of chemicals for nutrient sufficiency and insect/disease resiliency.

- Nature builds from the bottom-up with structures that are built to shape resulting in no waste. Humans cut-out the necessary materials from a stockpile, creating large amounts of trash.

- Nature uses abundant materials and energy, recycling the products to form a cyclic process. Humans use scarce metals and fossil fuels until they are depleted or the market deems them uneconomical.

As a link in the evolutionary chain, humans are a part of nature; therefore, human actions and designs are a part of the natural world. For the past 10,000 years, however, with the advent of the Agricultural Revolution, humans have been operating outside of the preceding basic ecological laws, leading to the current predicament of human culture teetering on the verge of ecological disaster.

Once the digressions of the human industrial designs have been realized, how do we improve upon them so we can operate within ecological boundaries? An emerging field of science, called biomimicry, seeks to answer precisely this question. At its essence, biomimicry is a look at nature through the eyes of a five-year old. By combining the unbounded curiosity of a child with the rigorous methods of a scientist, biomimicry analyzes nature's best ideas with the hope of implementing them into human designs. Although this nascent science has yet to be embraced on a broad scale by the designers of human systems, the results are already breathtaking.

Several years ago industrial designer Jay Harman, the visionary founder and CEO of Pax Scientific, noticed a fundamental pattern recurring in nature. Whether it was the shape of a funnel cloud or the blueprints of a seashell, the arrangement of spiral galaxies or the design of the inner ear, Harman realized fluids in nature always follow the same spiral path and that nature has optimized its designs to accommodate this physical law. Following this discovery, Harman developed the Pax Principle based on the natural flow pattern and by applying it to turbines, pumps, and propellers, huge savings were immediately realized. To the astonishment of many who spurned him, Harman's designs using the Pax Principle are more efficient, use less material, and are quieter than the designs that fluvial engineers have been developing for decades.

When Ray Anderson, CEO of Interface, the world's largest carpet manufacturer, decided to move his company towards sustainability, biomimicry caught his attention. Through the collaborative efforts of designers working with biologists, a new carpet design has revolutionized the entire structure of Interface. This new carpet, dubbed *Entropy*, utilizes a modular design that mimics the irregularities of the forest floor. When regular wear or a stain causes carpet to be replaced, *Entropy* owners can swap in a carpet tile at random without having to replace the entire carpet, as there is no pattern to adhere to, resulting in less waste. *Entropy* has become Interface's main product, currently accounting for 60% of the company's sales. Biomimicry has proven to be an economic success for Interface. Financial profits, combined with a commitment to environmentally-conscious industrial processes, have made Interface the leader of the global pack when it comes to corporate sustainability.

The Eastgate Building, an innovative high-rise built in the sweltering urban climate of Harare, Zimbabwe, was designed by mimicking the blueprints of perhaps nature's best builder, the termite. Inside a termite mound, the insects farm a fungus that must be kept at an optimum temperature. This is accomplished through a complex structural design that uses air currents to draw wet, warm air from the internal chambers. The architects who designed the Eastgate Building were able to mimic the termites' designs, resulting in an office-building located in southern Africa that utilizes no air conditioning system, yet maintains a constant temperature of 86° F throughout the year. The economic impacts have been enormous: the building owners saved $3.5 million by eliminating the air conditioning system and the electricity consumption is a meager 10% of buildings similar in size, resulting in tenant rents being an average 20% lower than buildings next door.

Although technological wonders abound in the natural world, integrating them into our industrial society is not easy. It involves, as Wes Jackson would say, "a world view based on ignorance rather than intelligence." An ignorance-based world view recognizes that, although humans have made significant discoveries, especially since the beginning of the scientific revolution in the sixteenth century, we are still "billions of times more ignorant than knowledgeable and always will be."

Instead of blindly pursuing development with the faith that human inventiveness will be able to carry the day, maybe we should humbly ask our natural neighbors for advice. At the end of her book *Biomimicry*, Janine Benyus outlines three ideas of how this process can begin: through silencing, echoing, and stewarding. For biomimicry to work we must quiet our busy minds and listen to what nature has to say. After meditating upon these ideas for awhile, we can then use our powerful brains to implement new technologies that fit smoothly into Ecosystem Earth. Finally, in order to preserve the millions of yet undiscovered natural ideas out there, our exploitative tendencies must be transformed into a conservation ethic.

In John McPhee's book, *Encounters with the Archdruid*, an account is given illustrating the wonderful storytelling-prowess of the late David Brower. McPhee writes:

Sooner or later in every talk, Brower describes the creation of the world. He invites his listeners to consider the six days of Genesis as a figure of speech for what has in fact been four billion years. On this scale, one day equals something like six hundred and sixty-six million years, and thus, all day Monday and until Tuesday noon, creation was busy getting the world going. Life began Tuesday noon, and the beautiful organic wholeness of it developed over the next four days. At 4 p.m. Saturday, the big reptiles came on. At three minutes before midnight on the last day, man appeared. At one-fourth of a second before midnight, the Industrial Revolution began. We are surrounded with people who think that what we have been doing for that one-fourth of a second can go on indefinitely. They are considered normal, *but they are stark, raving mad.*

Designing a better way for humans to live on this Earth through the use of novel ideas such as those encountered in biomimicry will enable us to transition from a world dominated by those who are "stark, raving mad." These people vociferously beat their chests while holding up the wheel as evidence of human technological prowess. What they fail to see is that nature quietly proves the existence of an alternate path.

Kendra Kellogg

BELMONT STOP

New tar, late sky
Drag purity in swallows
Push at smokestacks
This is my numb vista
I have pulled this view in less harmed

They stare across a long, rectangular subway sign
A bright marquis
Lights holding fast to a forked over million
Row by row like icicles

It's hard to know
Which coats are made from flesh
Supple as the sky
Ebbing through factory yards
Exhaling silt-breath

Tonight
Silent deeds nourish each gait dodging train doors
Hands raised to Armani faces
Shined shoes reflecting a dusk that began with your fist

I slide up Sedgwick
Through dry wall, glass block
Watch her hooves feeling hollow drums below
Her ribboned mane combs the air

In her lashed cornea
Resides a notched post of flung riders
Swift jabs from the inside
Leave kneecaps that never mend
Leave a leisurely limp
Breeding axles, cruise control
Asphalt, sewers
Exhaust grips my tongue
Like those who non-exist

Blair Oliver

Eldorado

Lucy's cat had been stolen by the woman across the street. It was my job to get him back. I didn't like the cat, but what choice did I have? My wife was an angel. She belly-danced. She danced after work at the Indian restaurant in town, and for me, late at night on our porch, hidden from the street by the trees, whose leaves cradled the moonlight. Once she raised her shirt overhead and swayed her starry hips so slowly back and forth that I pulled her atop me on the swing like I deserved her, like we were good people who had made all the right choices. Our lives were still ahead of us.

In a past life, the house across the street was a Victorian, but the neighbors had remodeled it so thoroughly that it was now Victorian in name only. There was an attached, three-car garage, for a BMW and a SUV, and a picket fence with a gate. There was a lawn-jockey. At night the lights burned, and guests in formal black came and went. The lady of the house was a member of leagues, committees, task forces. People like them were moving in from Texas and California, renovating and rebuilding. The block was littered with out-of-state plates, and our little bungalow, with my old boat and shed, was being swallowed whole. But everything worked—I'd always made sure of that. Still, I got letters from the new homeowners' association about cutting the grass, raking the leaves, or getting rid of the camper I kept under the carport alongside the house. I ignored these.

I'd lost my construction business years ago. At twenty-three, flush with my first big money, I played the market. Those early forays were remarkably successful. That was the problem. I was lucky, but I didn't know that then. It ended when it cost me my first wife. After I went broke, she left for a telecommunications executive in Denver. One time my ex called from the executive's office and said she missed me but strongly believed things happened for a reason. I told her I believed this too and she said either I didn't understand or I was mocking her. We shared a long quiet.

"Every person, every event has an energy," she'd said. "We have to be in tune with those forces to avoid imbalances."

"Who are you?" I asked.

"I believe in abundance, Mike, you know that."

One dug in or was kicked loose, like a forgotten satellite.

When I first went across the street for the cat, the people's garage door started to rise. I froze with my hand on the gate. The back of the woman's head filled the window as she eased her sedan down the drive. Her hair was piled high, and her collar was up. Her head looked like it was framed by large blue wings, and over her shoulder next to it was her white dog, staring out the back. Lately, I'd developed a fear of confrontations. At the post office I'd asked the clerk, a small man with pale, nervous hands, if he had a sponge I could use to seal my envelopes, and he looked me in the eyes and told me to lick them. Time was I would've clutched the clerk by the throat until he stopped breathing, but I'd had to do some work on my anger. Instead, my mouth went dry and I felt like I was losing my legs. The older I got the less sure of myself I was becoming.

So I let go of the woman's gate and strolled down the sidewalk. Her dog barked, but I didn't turn around.

That afternoon while I was in the kitchen doing my crossword I told Lucy the people weren't home again when I went over there. It had been two days since we noticed the cat was missing and she'd seen it in the people's window.

"That's all right," she said, closing the refrigerator door with her hip. She wore a tank-top and shorts. "You'll take care of it, baby."

She really was something. She was half my age, only twenty-one. God knows! Her parents died when she was a kid, and this seemed to make her inordinately susceptible to small kindnesses, the ones I was good for, like notes beneath the pillow, Cracker Jack gifts. Instead of being angry with me for this setback with the cat, she thanked me for trying. Unbelievable. Even when I stayed out late with Eddie Liberty, the owner of a crane outfit and my last buddy from the old days—in short, a man Lucy didn't trust—she left out a pot of coffee for me. Those nights I'd sit alone in the kitchen with my coffee and a crossword and listen to the creaks and pops of our house. I'd get mad then, at Lucy, for being so forgiving. I'd struggle to complete the puzzles as my heart raced in the dark.

"Don't you miss Sugar Ray?" I asked her.

She started cracking eggs in a bowl to scramble them.

"Heck," she said, "he's probably better off with them. Indoors. Milk."

"But he's yours. He's ours."

"What about your allergies?"

I'd been feigning allergies since we met—notes from the doctor, shots. None of this had convinced Lucy to give up the cat. She vacuumed daily.

"This isn't about me," I said.

Lucy craned at me from her spot next to the stove. Her hair fell across her mouth, and she blew at it.

"You never liked Sugar Ray," she said. "You should be happy."

Who did like the prospect of a cat, of history of any kind, moving in with his wife? Sugar Ray would disappear for days at a time, then show up on the back stoop bloodied and limping only to heal and disappear again a few weeks later. I did respect him, but because of his profligate lifestyle, it was possible the cat had been with the people across the street longer than we thought.

"People can't just take other people's cats," I said, looking down at the crossword, still a maze of empty white squares. "That's not something people do."

Lucy turned. Her nipples beaded against her shirt, and egg threatened to drip from the fork she held at her side. "You know, honey," she said, "sometimes I think you force things just because you're afraid someone will think you're too afraid not to."

We were not one of those couples who had difficulty communicating. "That doesn't change the basic facts of the situation," I said.

"Sugar Ray'll come back when he's ready."

"It's a matter of principles."

Lucy approached, then kissed me on the forehead. She let her lips linger there, and I felt her heat and the stirring. Then she looked over my shoulder toward the crossword.

"Jealousy," she said.

"What?"

"Thirteen down. It's jealousy."

Lucy had a few years at the community college. I turned and looked at the puzzle. *Green-eyed monster*. It wasn't something I could look up in one of my dictionaries. I'd been reading dictionaries and the thesaurus for years.

"Shakespeare," she shrugged, going back to the stove.

I stared at the back of her, at the fall of her dark hair between her bare, freckled shoulders, the way the light made a halo there, and at her bottom snug in her jeans. My throat tightened, and I wanted to believe her. I wanted to believe *in* her.

"Are you cold?" I said. "Would you like me to hold you?"

"What are you saying?" she asked, slowly stirring the eggs.

"Tell me you're cold," I said.

"I'll be late for work, baby."

I looked from her back to my puzzle. The questions were relentless. What was an eleven-letter word for chance? I gripped my pen and carefully filled in the blanks.

The next morning I went back across the street. Winding through the gate, I moved up the walk to the door and used the brass knocker. I stuffed my hands in my pockets. It was warm, hazy, late spring, and throughout the neighborhood people were waking and collecting their newspapers or washing their cars or weeding along the curbs. I turned back to the door but no one came. Someone was moving inside the house—I could hear it—but the door remained closed. I knocked again, this time louder, more insistently.

She opened the door in her red silk robe. Her hair was still piled high, but it was loosening, tangled from sleep. She was in her thirties, I thought, and attractive, but in a way that required effort, which she seemed willing to give. She had bullied her way to pretty

"Can I help you, Mr. Binder?" she asked, spine-straight despite having just woken.

I was supposed to say something then. I was supposed to be angry. Part of me hoped I wouldn't have to say anything, that by just showing up she'd know what this was about and quietly hand over the cat.

"Is everything all right?" she asked. "Is your wife okay?"

I pulled my hands from my pockets. She looked beyond me, toward my house, and I knew what she saw there, how her dreams and mine were not the same. She didn't see a place I'd earned with my back, a home where I'd loved and lost and loved again. Where I'd been loved. Rather, she saw an eyesore, an embarrassment to her friends.

I asked if she'd seen our cat.

"Sugar Ray has feline leukemia, Mr. Binder."

"That's bullshit," I said, before I could stop myself.

The woman put her hand on the side of the door as if to close it. Behind her, I could just make out the edge of a sofa, a settee it was called, and the short hall leading back to the kitchen and family room. There, the white dog lay smugly on the hardwood.

"I have to ask you to leave."

"Is the man of the house in?" I asked. "Is there someone I can talk to here?"

"Jerry's at the gym," she said. "Jerry's a runner. And I resent the implication."

"Look," I said, "I know that cat's perfectly fine and I'm willing to forget this whole thing if I can just have him back. If you want me to, I'll leave right now, and you can go around back, let him out, and let him decide."

"I took the cat to the vet," she said. "He has cancer. You let him run around the neighborhood and he's a danger to himself as well as to others. If you'd cared for him, you'd have noticed how anemic he is. You're lucky I don't report you."

I wondered if what she said about the cat was true. "I've recently had him to the vet myself," I said, lying now. "He's an outdoor cat. Open the door and let him decide."

"Goodbye, Mr. Binder," she said, shutting the door.

Eddie Liberty ordered another round, then picked at the pile of cold nachos on the bar between us, alongside our darts.

"The cat didn't come back?" he said.

"She didn't give him a chance."

He shook his head and cupped the whiskey the bartender brought him. The gold medallion, a family heirloom, hung from his open neck and swung above his glass. Blonde hair, like some kind of mad growth, sprouted from his chest, springing up through the collar of his purple Hawaiian shirt so that no clear line existed between his chest hair and three-day beard.

Businessmen sat at the tables behind us, smoking and drinking Manhattans with their bloody steaks. Fanning out around us at the bar, a few old men alternately stared into their drinks and mumbled awkward come-ons to the waitress, while one small boy spun around his father's table, crunching the spent peanut shells on the floor.

"Maybe the cat's better off," Eddie Liberty said. "He was sick, wasn't he?"

"A bit anemic maybe, but that comes with the territory." I shifted on my stool to get more comfortable. My crosswords were stuffed in my back pocket. "He's a scamp," I said.

"Cheers."

I'd known Eddie Liberty since our principal's-office days in grade school. Now, he was a captain of industry. His garage was two stories high so he could keep one of his cranes with him at home. When I still had my business, we did a few jobs together, gas stations and fast food joints. Every "Arby's" in the state was ours. After both of our divorces, we lived together off of St. Thomas where we ran a club for the tourists who'd clamber in from the cruise ships to marvel at the alcoholic snake that hung from our rafters and drank rum shots off of the bar. Eddie's brother ran the crane outfit while we wore Hawaiian shirts, swung in hammocks, and played bumper pool with island girls. Soon, though, Eddie Liberty had to return home before his brother lost the business. He smuggled in a quiver of hollow surf rods packed with uncut cocaine to pay off the notes on the remaining cranes, and I followed shortly thereafter, moving to the next town over. What I found when I got back was that none of my old friends or partners wanted to know me anymore. All of them except Eddie Liberty, that is, who still wore Hawaiian shirts.

"So what are you going to do about it?" he asked. "The cat."

"Wait until her husband gets home and reason with him."

"Reason? What reason? I remember when you never would've let yourself be handcuffed by reason. These aren't reasonable people."

"It's a matter of principles," I said.

He tucked his medallion inside his shirt.

"Stealing cats is not something civilized people do," he said, picking up one of the darts and tapping its point into the bar. The teak was pocked with holes. He let go of the dart and turned to me on his stool. Usually we'd talk to each other's reflections in the warped mirror above the booze, so when he did that I had to swivel to meet his eyes. It took both of us a moment to adjust. He stared at me, as if he were trying to find something he couldn't quite make out. Then whatever it was he was looking for he seemed to find and turned back to the mirror. In the funhouse glass, the flowers on Eddie Liberty's shoulders bloomed then curled again like they were dying.

"I know your neighbor," he said.

"Mrs. Hewlett?"

"I was on the task force to change the high school's team name. It was offensive to women."

In the islands, he'd bed Catholic girls on their Easter vacations.

"You know, Mike, you could use some sensitivity training yourself." His medallion got loose again and spun over his drink. "Just last month I had my whole crew go on a retreat. Duffy, Jack, all of them. Sure they bitched, but I caught them hooting at women passing the job site." He clapped the medallion to his chest. "At the retreat we drew pictures. We made a quilt out of all the pictures we drew about the times we felt different, about our safe places."

"Who's the new girlfriend?" I asked.

"She was passing by the job site. No, don't laugh. It was a real learning experience. I'm telling you, I'm a changed man. We played a game in which we were evil if we tried to win. You need to hear this."

I plumed the feathers on one of the darts. The crossword I'd been working on when Eddie Liberty picked me up was only half-finished. I needed a twenty-letter phrase for government scandal. The answer would break open the entire puzzle.

We finished our drinks and acquired more, putting them on Eddie Liberty's tab. I asked if he could come up with the phrase. He wondered why I just didn't turn to the answer key.

"Because it's not ethical," I said.

He looked directly at me again, like he had before, then slumped on his stool.

"Why don't I talk to Mrs. Hewlett for you? Your anniversary's this weekend, isn't it?"

Eddie Liberty was the best man at both of my weddings. While this troubled my wives, he took such duties gravely. I made a note to call for reservations. Perhaps I'd get an advance from the grill for a night in Central City. Lucy and I could play a little blackjack, have drinks on the house and eat at the buffet, then take in the opera, which she liked.

"Yes, it's our anniversary."

"I'll smooth things over with the neighbors and you two songbirds can have the condo for the weekend."

He had a plush, three-bedroom condo, creekside in Vail. Lucy wouldn't like the idea, but I could convince her. Then I remembered our car was in the shop, but I thought Eddie Liberty knew that too, as he'd picked me up to come to the bar.

"Sounds nice," I said, "but I think we'll stay in town."

"Look," he said, touching my arm, "if Lucy's doesn't want to stay at my place—"

"It's our car."

"Hell, take my car. I don't know what Lucy has against me, other than the usual objections, but she's a wonderful lady. You ought to take her away. You don't want to screw up with this one."

I closed my crossword.

"The Eldorado, Mike. Think about it."

That night, I slipped from bed, threw on black, and went into the kitchen. My crossword was open on the table. The white squares, the missing twenty-letter word at the center—that vast emptiness—haunted me. I passed it, almost vengefully, took an open can of tuna from the refrigerator and sneaked across the street.

The moon was on its back in the trees. I walked up the Hewlett's drive and nearly jumped when the floodlight above the garage burst upon me. I'd known it had a motion sensor, but in my excitement I'd forgotten. I looked up to what I thought must be their bedroom window, how the edge of the light illuminated the great panes, and waited. No one moved. Regaining my breath, I ducked into the alley between the garage and fence and made my way to the backyard.

The Hewlett's yard, of course, was immaculate. It seemed that there, suddenly, summer had arrived. Large, moonstruck flowers nodded along the fence. Jerry Hewlett would stroll his grounds with a glass of lemonade, watching the hired Mexicans weed, cut and edge the grass, replace wood chips and repair the arbor, prune hedges, change fountain filters, and plant new trees. Now the fountains gurgled pleasantly. Venus and Cupid. The marble mother reached out for her son, who, with taut bow, stayed teasingly out of reach in the arbor. I almost turned back, feeling every bit the clumsy intruder. Two more lights went on as I stepped into the yard.

The white dog was staring at me from the stoop. I froze in the center of the light. The dog, a Bichon Frise I noted, had his own door through which he could exit and reenter the house. Putting a finger to my lips, I glanced around the yard for Lucy's cat. Beyond the lights, nothing stirred in the darkness.

I removed the tuna from my pocket and offered it to the dog. Still, he just sat there, primly. Then I stepped out of the light to see what would happen. He didn't follow me. I took a few more steps, almost against the house now, but the dog still stared straight ahead to where the lights made bright disks in the grass. Sugar Ray wasn't along the fence or in the low branches of the trees. Then I moved quickly back to my left and the dog only cocked his head, listening.

He was blind. As I approached, he sniffed at the air and growled. Above him, inside the window, I saw the cat. I held out the tuna to the dog, and he tested it, hesitantly at first, then dug in. That's when I scooped him up, clamped his muzzle, and hurried from the yard.

Lucy began packing the next morning for our trip to the mountains. At first she was adamant about not going, recycling her old charges about Eddie Liberty's lack of morals, his bad influence, etc., etc., but I promised we'd pay for the condo. Soon, she was trying on swimsuits for the hot tub, parading above me and the dog on the bed. She didn't give me a hard time about the dog. Somewhere along the line, in the various homes she'd stayed in after her parents had died, she became less scrupulous about minor improprieties. Unlike me, Lucy wasn't concerned the dog didn't mind spending the night away from his family, just as Sugar Ray hadn't run back to us the first chance he had. Disloyalty didn't surprise her. She'd spent part of the morning teaching the dog our floor plan. After crashing into several walls, the dog was a quick study.

Resting at the curb was Eddie Liberty's 1976 Cadillac Eldorado. He must've dropped it off before heading to work. In a couple of hours, Lucy and I would take a spin with the top down through the old part of town. The car was gold, and like Raleigh, I'd allow myself to imagine something better for Lucy and me was just over the horizon. I had to start keeping the promises of the man she married.

But now, from behind our bedroom curtains, we watched our frantic neighbors calling for their pet. They nailed posters to the telephone polls. They formed search parties.

"Do you think we should tell them?" Lucy asked me.

"Hell, no," I said.

The three of us got back in bed where I decided Eddie Liberty was in such a generous mood I'd talk to him about lending me the money to get on my feet again. I'd been reluctant because I didn't want money to get in the way of our friendship, as it apparently had with so many others, but seeing how excited the upcoming trip made my wife I knew I had to risk it. I didn't understand yet that Lucy was the only person I'd ever underestimated, and that, like every one of my mistakes, every goddamned one, was going to cost me.

"Give me a twenty-letter phrase for government scandal," I said, petting the blind dog.

Lucy straddled my legs. "Watergate, Nanny-gate, Travel-gate—"

"Iran-Contra…."

"Oh, who cares?" she said, closing the curtain and falling on top of me.

We locked the dog inside with food and water and went for our afternoon drive before I took Lucy to work. When I returned, a long, black Buick on gold rims was parked in front of the house across the street. Eddie Liberty had said he was going to talk to the woman, but this wasn't one of his cars, nor was it the kind of car any of the woman's friends would own. I wondered if they'd hired a private dick to locate their pet or if they were calling in the muscle to shake me down.

As I was mixing a drink, a rare knock sounded on my door. I peeked through the window and saw Mrs. Hewlett and her husband in his warm-up suit with Sugar Ray squirming in the awkward cradle of his arms.

The cat was uncomfortable, but he didn't look half as agitated as my normally composed neighbors.

"Can I help you?" I said, opening the door.

"I believe we have something of yours," Mrs. Hewlett stammered. The cat sprang from Jerry's arms and ran past me into the house. I felt sorry for Jerry; clearly his wife had led him over by the ear. Then the dog began to bark in the kitchen.

"Is that Max?"

"Who?"

"Max!" Mrs. Hewlett shouted.

The dog trotted around the corner and ran straight into the wall in the hallway. I braced for Mrs. Hewlett's fists, but all of us stood still in the threshold, watching Max. He crossed the floor and bumped into the opposite wall before righting his course and sprinting for the door between my legs.

"Oh, Max, you had us so worried," Mrs. Hewlett said, catching up her dog.

I looked at Jerry. He seemed more nervous than angry. She must have really given it to him.

"Look, we're terribly sorry about this," he said. "We've made a mistake."

"I'll say," I said, seizing the momentum.

"A simple misunderstanding," Mrs. Hewlett said. She hugged and kissed the dog. She looked like she might cry. Maybe more had happened than I realized, that someone had died or that Eddie Liberty really did scare them. Maybe Jerry owed somebody some money.

"Is everything all right?" I asked.

"Yes. Quite all right," Jerry said. He paused. "You have your cat back now. What do you say we forget the whole thing?"

I looked past them to the street. It was empty, save for the Eldorado. My porch swing creaked in the breeze. The three of us stood together for a moment longer. We'd been neighbors for two years, and we'd never done that before. I wasn't sure what was happening, but I was willing to believe in a happy ending.

"Thanks for returning Sugar Ray," I finally said.

"And here's his medicine," Mrs. Hewlett said, reaching over Max and into her pocket. She handed over a bottle of pills. "He takes one of these a day."

"Preventative?"

"Vitamins, really."

I couldn't reach Eddie Liberty, but the next afternoon the condo keys arrived inside an anniversary card. We called a pet sitter for Sugar Ray, as I didn't want him to miss his pills, and left.

Our big car thundered up the foothills and into the mountains. Lucy curled in the crook of my arm and put her feet on the dash, where the sun sparked off her red-painted toes. The high snow was melting, and the crevices and chutes were slick with runoff. Near Georgetown, bighorns grazed alongside the road.

After unpacking, Lucy started the jets in the tub out on the deck. She settled in with champagne. Her body glowed in the underwater lights, and above her, the first few stars winked in the void. Aspens shivered. I sat on the rim in one of Eddie Liberty's monogrammed robes and closed the crossword puzzle in my lap. We were ready for a slow, good night. Just as I dipped my foot into the water, someone knocked on the living room door.

"Let them knock," Lucy said, reaching out her hand. The down on her arm was covered with tiny bubbles.

I squeezed her and tied my robe as I went inside. At the door was a large, dark man, Colombian, I learned later, in a suit. He kept his meaty hands folded before him as he spoke.

"Are you Mr. Eddie Liberty?" he asked, his accent thick.

"Can I help you?"

He grinned as if I knew what he was there for, like I may have been expecting him and the game was over.

"Is this your condominium?" he said, stepping by me into the living room.

I looked past him to the sliding door I'd left open behind the curtain. I could see the light there. I could hear the jets.

"This isn't what you think," I said. Blood pumped in my temples as the man glanced about the room, at the paintings on the wall and the pottery on the shelves. The ink from my puzzle was coming off in my hand. "I have to ask you to leave."

"Very nice," he said. "Expensive, no?" His waxed hair gleamed in Eddie Liberty's recessed lighting. He turned to look at me, and I saw something heavy in his belt. "How much they pay you?"

"What?"

"To turn state's evidence."

"Look," I said, moving between him and the sliding door, "I really don't—"

"Shush," he said. He put his finger to his lips, then nodded. "Is that your car out front? Tags: Liberty?"

The Buick, I thought. The gold rims. I was trying hard now. The answers were coming to me. I turned back to the curtain and saw Lucy's shadow, her silhouette dancing beyond it. She raised her arms overhead and swayed slowly in the tub. Both of us watched her like that, and as my heart rose in my throat, I thought the older I got, the fewer friends I had.

BRIAN KITELEY
SONG OF NORTH HAMPTON

*This is a selection from **The River Gods**, a history of Northampton, Massachusetts. Much of the book moves backwards through time, meeting up with the same characters every once in a while, but mostly introducing new historical figures and anonymous characters with each small segment of time. The interlaced method of history and fiction I use splices rewritten documents and interstitial fictions between apparent facts and historical figures.*

November 1993
Some Northampton Street Names

First Square, Fourth, Fifth, Paradise, Florence, Bliss, Young Rainbow, Old Rainbow, Fairfield, Fern, Locust, Myrtle, Maple, Elm, Audubon, Evergreen, Woodlawn, Dryads Green, Spring, Linden, Walnut, Olive, Cherry, Orchard, Lawn, Cooke, Fruit, Burts Pit, Swan, Riverside, Rust, North Farms, West Farms, Mt. Tom, Rocky Hill, South Pynchon Meadows, Meadow, Swamp, Nook, Curtis Nock, King, Kings, Gothic, Chapel, Fort, Pilgrim, Stoddard, Lyman, Parsons, Edwards, Pomeroy, Hawley, Forbes, Trumbull, Munroe, Calvin, West, Old Ferry, Bridge, Crescent, Prospect, Upland, Hillside, Lexington, Franklin, Washington, Madison, Harrison, Garfield, Taylor, Winter, Summer, Sumner, Lincoln, Grant, Northern, Sherman, Union, Graves, Liberty, Texas, Coolidge, Wilson, Kensington, Maynard, Jewell, Pearl, Green, Federal, Main, Front, Center, Market, Fort Hill, Cosmian, Masonic, Corticelli, Dickinson, Whittier, Ellington, Hollywood, Gleason, Ahwaga, Massasoit, Nonotuck.

May 1967
Interstate 91
Walter West, 41

In May 1967 the highway was finished but awaiting its final inspection. Mr. James was in Ohio near Columbus, with a stop in North Carolina between Winston-Salem and Statesville, before he could come here to this stretch between Springfield, Massachusetts and White River Junction, Vermont. Earl and I had free reign. The clean white surfaces, the road signs still draped in green canvas, the occasional hunter or hiker near the forested parts of the highway. We could drive as fast as the old Chevy truck would take us—not that fast. This segment of interstate was the longest opened in New England in many years. Usually Mr. James inspected five or ten-mile sections. This was eighty miles of untouched concrete and blacktop, finished but not commissioned for several months now. We patrolled the road between eight and five. Earl made me stop if there was the vaguest sighting of that skittish prey—woman. We would stand on bridges. Earl wanted to hoot or howl or at least stamp his feet, but all he did was stare. Once, in Northampton, a beautiful young thing was out stalking this quiet stretch of road that passed under the highway on the way to Easthampton. No houses or gas stations nearby. Why she was out like this, at nine in the morning? Something is happening to the kids these days. The boys have suddenly grown their hair out. The girls wear light, loose blouses with pastel flowers on them. Plus they're burning their bras or at least leaving them in the top drawer. This one was tall, dark-haired, wearing jeans and an almost sheer white shirt—her grampa's shirt washed so often it was losing cohesion. Her breasts were small, but it was like she was standing naked behind a gauze curtain. I called out, as Earl grabbed my wrist quite painfully, "M'am! Do you want to take a look at the new freeway? We're patrol agents of the Interstate Highway Commission." She looked up—she wasn't fifteen feet away—and I saw she was crying. But lo and behold she clambered up the gravel hillside and was standing with us on the bridge paving in no time. She looked about nineteen. Or maybe sixteen. Who could tell these days? They were growing up more quickly than we did, back in the day. Earl and I were both born on the same day, October 3, 1925. I suggested we drive the long loop around Northampton, which she said she'd grown up in, to see the town in a way it had never been seen by anyone before. Earl was stunned she accepted the invitation. If his daughter went out taking rides from complete strangers, even if they did have federal government identification, she'd hear a thing or two. Me, I don't have any kids, nor a wife lately. The girl acted as if she hadn't been crying and asked questions about the surface, the banking of the turns, the history of highways. She asked if it was true that Eisenhower had driven across country in 1919 in an army caravan, the first cross-country motor vehicle trek. I hadn't heard of that, but Earl grunted in the affirmative. He's always surprising me. Earl said it took the caravan sixty days to reach Los Angeles. He said the Lincoln Highway was the first cross-country road, connecting hundreds of little patches of country and county roads, zig-zagging crazily. The girl said her father thought Eisenhower was impressed by the German autobahns he saw after the war (her father was a private assigned to his command). We returned her to the overpass where we'd found her, and Earl asked, all fatherly concern suddenly, why she was crying at first. The girl laughed. "Free love," she said. We puzzled over this after she slid down the gravel to her road. The moment she was gone, Earl switched to the lecherous old man I loved and admired. "Free love," he snorted. "Ain't no such thing, but I'm game if she is."

1854
A Northamptonite Abroad, 30

Dear Mother,   October 14, 1854

I write from Reims, about eighty miles from Paris. You don't understand why I left Paris so quickly after arriving there. Paris offers untold riches and pleasures, but the purpose of these travels is to sample the smaller towns and cities, to get a whiff of the life of the average countryman, whom I feel will enable me to make happy contrasts with the industry, simplicity, and tenacity of Americans. Reims interests me particularly because of the Catholic martyr, Joan. I know, I know, you dislike my indulging in the practices and rituals of other religions. But surely our own cannot suffer from the comparison, can they? Besides, the teenage soldier virgin Joan of Arc seems a rather American phenomenon. She rose up out of nothing. She built an army by the force of her visions. She was sacrificed to the enemy by people of her own blood, more or less, in exchange for commerce and lucre. One can imagine her rising up from her Elm Street digs one morning to tend to her tomatoes and lettuces. One can picture the daughter of a grandson of Edwards, lax in her spiritual apprehension of the world, sweet-natured but not a terribly good Christian (forgive me), and she reaches down to pick up a ripe tomato, when, in a flash, she is felled by the word of God: "Go forth and lead the Unitarians back to my Home." Well, forgive a lonely son his fantasies.

I toured the church, famous because many French kings were baptized here as Kings. They say it is a magnificent structure. I certainly felt the weight of its stones, the lightness of its columns of rosy-colored air that continued unimpeded seventy feet heavenward, indoors. But it is all a lost world as far as I'm concerned, an overbuilt memorial to a God they've forgotten in the hubbub of their complex rituals and architecture. I prefer the First Church's simple pieties, its closer walls and worn wooden benches. I don't know. Sign me up for the Know-Nothings.

I saw a girl lighting a candle, dwarfed by the column she placed the candle on (in a metal holder). A tear rolled down her cheek and onto her slightly exposed bosom. She turned, saw me, gave a start, and her skin pinked. I imagined marrying her and bringing her home to the lush valley of my birth, setting her up, not in luxury, but with ample provisions, taking her away from this drab, ornate world. But when she passed I heard her say a prayer for me under her breath, a light and winsome wish that I find the true path—she sensed my cynicism or perhaps she recognized my American outfit. I was so repulsed by the thought of this girl feeling herself better off than me spiritually that I nearly grabbed a lock of her hair as she fled. In fact, the blond tress slipped through my fingers and left me with a startling sensation of loss, as if I'd buried my sister again, ten years later. She did not look back. Her fine perfume, an odor of death and apples, lingered in my nostrils, and I could recapture it for several hours after by touching a finger to my upper lip.

May 1653
One Who Won't Take the Covenant

We came here for Gold, not God. Spain and Portugal divided the new world, with the complicity of the Popes. The Moors drove them West looking for new spice routes to the Indies and China and the great Khan. The discovery of all the Gold in the southern Americas, but not here, drove down the price of Gold in Europe, further Bankrupting our treasuries, already devastated by the Black Death and the destitution of the lands of our Lords. The fall in the value of Gold (and I might say God) had the unforeseen Benefit of wiping out much of Othman's wealth in the Near East. He still pounded at Europe's back door, but it was clear the Turks would not be able to pay their soldiers long or buy land out from under us. The Kingdoms of Spain and Portugal mismanaged their trade, killing off or expelling their best tradesmen—the Arabs and the Jews. We stood by Gloating quietly. It was left to the Dutch and ultimately the British, staunch sea-faring Protestant nations both, to give the coup de grâce to Catholic Spain's pretensions of exclusive control of the old world, the new world, and the next world. Every once in a while, an English sailor was captured and trapped in the machinery of their Inquisition. When one English sailor—they dared call us pirates—escaped and reported the horrors to London, we redoubled our efforts against the papists.

In Virginia the Gold they Discovered was Tobacco, nearly as valuable. I confess to finding its taste vile. Further north, in New Holland, we tempted Fate. Furs, lumber, potatoes, and dried fish was all we could trade in—meager Lucre. I was there for the Establishment of the Hartford trading post, and I happened to be along for the Founding of Agawam, which Pynchon later called Springfield. The winters were harsh, but I judge the land and climate charming, in the end. To be at the edge of another Civilization pleases me in my old age. Pyncheon and his partners sold us the land of Nonotuck, out from under these Indians. There were 300 Indians and perhaps 100 Warriors among that number. The deed:

"All the said Premises the said Pynchon & his Assigns shall have & enjoy Absolutely & clearly forever, all Incumbrances from any Indians or their Cornfields. In Witness of this presents the said Indians have Subscribed their marks this 24th day of September, 1653. Pequahalent, Nanassahalent, Chickwallop, Nassicohee, Skittomp."

I will enjoy Nonotuck absolutely but not Forever. The Fanaticks who populate the Bay Colony drift out here, up the Connecticut. I am Weary of their own small Inquisitions in a patty-pan.

Clotilde Wright

Neighborhood Vignettes

1
Old red bike
overgrown with green
spokes and vines
entangled lovers
from lives past.

2
Economic samurai
blue shirt and tie
on motor bike rides
off to do battle with delicate hands.

3
A dog barks,
a slow car from behind,
a bike and then a distant train's rumbling.
Oh, a neighborhood side street.

solo 270-mile bicycle ride
22.5hours

1/2 oz mango cheeks (dried)

1veggie burger with lettuce and tomato on a bun

package potato chips

1 liter coca-cola

1 bean and cheese burrito

slept 6hours   strawberries,

6 fig newtons

1 oz mango cheeks (dried)

figs

1 green chile platter (2 tortillas,

2 ibuprofen

2 350ml cans coca-cola

1 350 ml beer

refried beans, cheese, green chile, medium)

1 snickers bar

payday bars (snack size)k size)

1 king size p

1 almond joy bar

package tums EX fruit flavor (calcium)

3 oz mango cheeks

2 buffered aspirin

chicken with fettuccini and a cream sauce

4 oz brown rice syrup

chocolate mousse

sa

1/2 liter orange juice

1.5 liter coca-cola

liter orange juice

solo 270-mile bicycle ride in

I ate, napped for 4 hours, walked the dogs, ate, went to the movies, and

Activity Notes: I slept 4h, and then rode

went to bed.

22.5 hours

I lost no weight over the ride, but I am still

1/2 liter orange juice

2 buffered a

avenous four days later.

Drizzle falls through the orange streetlamp glow. I outfit myself in walkable (mountain) shoes, a **wool jersey**, bib shorts, legwarmers, armwarmers, bandanna, long-fingered gloves, glove liners, and an ear band—adequate for the cool, rainy conditions. I ride my **touring bike**, modified with a double crankset and 28c tires. My touring bike is set up with handlebars even with the **seat top**, a Brooks saddle, a hub generator, SON E6 headlight, twin LED tail lamps, a Petzl LED helmet lamp, and a saddlebag. Fully loaded, with three full water bottles, luggage, and plenty of food on board, **the bike weighs 45lb.**

雷

by Alex Paozols

TAKO GA CHIBA O TABETA, A BAND OUT OF JAPAN, HAD SET SAIL ACROSS THE PACIFIC TO TOUR THE USA. BEFORE THE BAND'S DEPARTURE THE CREATURES FROM THE SKY ATTACKED KOREA, AUSTRALIA AND NEW ZEALAND. THE CREATURES THEN DROPPED GIANT NORI SUSHI FILLED WITH MUTANT SQUID AND OCTOPUS ON THE OCEAN LINER AND LAUNCHED A SECOND ATTACK WITH A MONSTOROUS SIX-EYED WHALE. THE BAND WAS FORCED TO STEP UP IN RESISTANCE. KOSUE, THE BASSIST, HAD HER COUSIN TSU' SEND AN ARMY OF ALBATROS. WHEN THE BIRDS SLICED OPEN THE WHALE MORE MUTANT OCEAN LIFE SPILLED OUT—BUT THEY WERE NO MATCH FOR TSU'S UNCANNY CREATIONS.

AFTER THE BATTLE WAS WON THE HALF-ROBOT ALBATROS AIR LIFTED THE CORPSES INTO THE PACIFIC. THE BAND PLAYED FOR THE CAPTAIN AND HER HUSBAND THAT NIGHT. SOON THEY ARRIVED IN SAN FRANCISCO. ON HER FIRST DAY IN THE BAY CITY KOSUE WENT SHOPPING AT THRIFT STORES WITH BAND-MATE NORIKO.

NORIKO FOUND A MR. T T-SHIRT AT THE WISHING WELL FOR $2.

BURP!

MEANWHILE, NASA RELEASED SATELLITE PHOTOS OF THE UNDERWATER SPACE STATION BUILT BY THE CREATURES FROM THE SKY. POWERED BY SEAWEED, IT WAS NESTLED IN A GODFORSAKEN VALLEY OFF THE COAST OF SRI LANKA.

THROUGHOUT THE MURKY DEPTHS OF THE PACIFIC A FLEET OF STINGRAY BATTLESHIPS AND ROBOT SHARKS SET OUT ON A PATH OF EVIL.

KOSUE'S COUSIN TSU SET OUT ON HIS CUSTOM-MADE MORIMOTO-77 TO EXPLORE THE OCEAN BEFORE THE NEXT ATTACK. HE LISTENED TO A SPECIAL MIX BY THE CUT-UP BOYS ON HIS SHIKONPOD, WHICH PUT HIM IN FOCUS. IT CONTAINED SONGS BY DOGZILLA, TIESTA AND MARS 69.

THE MEDIA SIMPLY DUBBED THE INVADERS AS "THE CREATURES." WORLD LEADERS CALLED FOR UNITY AND PEACE. THE PRESIDENT OF THE USA PLAYED GOLF.

TSU DEPLOYED HEAVILY-ARMED UNDERWATER MECHABOTS WHO WERE ACCOMPANIED BY A POSSE OF GIANT SEALS.

NORIKO RECEIVED A TEXT MESSAGE FROM KIYOSHI.

THEIR SONG "THUNDER" WAS NUMBER ONE IN JAPAN.

THE SHOW IN L.A. SOLD OUT. KOSUE SANG LIKE A BUTTERFLY.

RRRRMMMM....

PORTLAND THEN SEATTLE. SHOWS IN DENVER, PHOENIX AND ALBUQUERQUE CANCELLED DUE TO RASH METEOR ATTACKS.

TSU SENT A SQUAD OF DEFENDERS TO THE USA TO PROTECT THE BAND.

ISHIBAYASHI SCORED A HALF OF KIND IN LAWRENCE, KANSAS DURING A SHOW AT KÚ.

A MASSIVE MULTI-VOLCANO DISASTER IN KYUSHU, JAPAN TRIGGERED BY THE CREATURES. DEATH TOLL IS WICKED

TRANSFORMERS ARE DISPATCHE BY THE USA. THE CREATURES ARE KEEN TO THEIR DESIGN AND CREATE ROBOTS THAT ARE ANALOGOUS. AN EVACUATION IS ORDERED IN LOWER TEXAS.

MILK MAN DEERHOOF

CHICAGO. OPENED FOR THE STROKES. KOSUE AND NORIKO DRESS IN KOSUPURE FASHION FOR A NIGHT ON THE TOWN.

THE BAND ATTENDS A DEERHOOF SHOW IN DETROIT WITH KIYOSHI'S COUSIN ASOBI. THEY MEET HAVOC, OF MOBB DEEP, AT THE SHELTER, A HIP HOP CLUB.

IN NASHVILLE NORIKO CALLS HER BOYFRIEND TOJI. HER HOME ISLAND HOKKAIDO WAS PILLAGED BY THE CREATURES.

HER FAMILY ESCAPED BY FERRY. TOJI'S BROTHERS REMAINED TRAPPED IN A TUNNEL ON THE NOZOMI TRAIN. UKIYO-E PAINTINGS FROM EDO WERE DESTROYED BY SUMO-BOTS.

TOJI WAS SKILLED IN THE ART OF IAIDO. HE COULD NOT SLEEP.

無印良品は

Genevieve Betts

Swallowing Stone

His car smells of fireworks,
the same ones that sit
on my shelf,
they hear rain
and know that now
is not the time.

They want to spin
electric fire crumbs
that cannot singe away
        the feeling one has of leaving
an incenced lover behind —
white bones burn to ash
in seconds.

Sisyphus,
pushing the boulder
centered in my maw
aches.

The cave through which it came,

a crazy eight
        through circle of teeth,

        holy,

catapulting snake and tongue.

It rolls back down my pile
of stones,
hits the liver
hard,

old relics
intoxicate me,
make me forget
the rocks
I'll vomit later.

From the drizzle-soaked, **silent** and bleak start at the US 36/ Superior Park-n-ride, I head east to Brighton on CO 7. Large, empty suburban parking lots are always eerie. Why do they leave all the street lights on at **4am?** To replace the sounds of crickets, who do not **find asphalt viable habitat**, with the buzz of the sodium vapor lamps. It is mostly downhill and the gently rolling hills of the plains do not present much challenge. The rain subsides, and the clouds slowly retreat as the morning wears on. Due to our unseasonably wet weather, the fields are very green, reminiscent of Virginia in late spring, but land here is disappearing under the burden of **identical, expensive houses.**

Steven Church

Unpublished Letter to the Editor from Eldest of the Holnam Sisters

"Cement Kiln or Incinerator? No Holnams Barred"[1]

"(Note: The author is a member of the Holnam's Community Advisory Committee. The views expressed here do not reflect the views of the committee or any of its other members.)"

(Note: The author is not a member of the Holnam's Community Advisory Committee. The views expressed here do not reflect views. Refract perhaps. Retire, retread.)

"Cement kilns have become America's incinerators, one in every community."

But what do we burn? You want to know? Fingers of rebar. Bodies of concrete. The bones of streets. You ask, does the Captain bathe me regularly? Does he burn tires too? Does he shell eggs with a penknife in the mornings before we children wake for work? We don't ask, for fear he might not recognize the asker. Have you ever seen him hate a stray dog?

"No plume or groundwater contamination to be traced, no legal liability. Into the air and everywhere, contaminants become part of our bodies. We pass the genetic damage to our grandkids."

You want to know how you trace plume? Is it from the feathers they drop? The Captain bought a peacock to keep us company. All day we shovel cement. All night we shovel rubber. The peacock struts free around the yard, chortling and cooing at us. When dusk gives way to night, we hear his talons click-clicking on the wooden porch.

This is family cement business.

You never go against the family.

"From around the country come cries for help. From Bozeman . . . comes a call: Holnam is trying to burn tires."

Quitting time for Captain. He thumbs a matchbook. Sits on the porch, stroking his bird. Evening apple in hand. He rocks, rocks, watches us girls. Callers don't tread over now. No trace of contaminants. The Captain burns what he wants in the dark. Tosses them to the pile.

> *Lo, but I have seen the mound.*
>
> > *And it is smoldering tonight as I whisper to you through the fence that separates us.*
>
> *For him, the bird dances in the dirt. Spreads her plume and shakes the colors loose.*
>
> *For us, the TV burn of a tire fire is all we have.*

"Ten years ago, Bozeman fought hazardous waste burning and won."

Don't you look at us and walk away. Captain preaches with promises: clean sheets, hot water, toothpaste. His heart on fire with lies. Burning rubber doesn't crackle. But it roars. What makes his waste hazardous is not speed, not quick feet, but reach — the long arms of stink. Captain quick trigger, puncher, a bullet-dancer sees all from the porch. Wooden rocker, back and forth. He shadowboxed for the title once. Keeps a scared pistol in his pants. Now he hardly leaves his corner.

"Communities unite to fight Holnam."

Statement of fact, a command? What do you want to hear? "Burn rubberman, burn." The Captain can't see Bozeman coming, can't see the waste like the sisters can. We whisper round the kilns, tell stories of Bozeman's horse. Silver Guns. Leather Chaps. Rifle slung through a saddle loop.

"Right now, the really dangerous chemicals coming out of Holnam are ignored and will be ignored with tire burning."

Because we can't help gathering at the glow. Burning orange and black and thick. The Holnam Sisters sing fire songs. Roasting smores — as we wait for him to sleep. His vigilant bird still struts on guard. We're ignorant as we hold our palms to the rubber heat. We are girls, our dresses stained with his soot.

We roll another tire into the fire, don't notice the smell anymore.

"The most dangerous chemicals are those that persist, or break down slowly, and bioaccumulate. (Eat a fish, keep the fish's chemicals.) Some chemicals cause cellular mutations that are then passed on to future generations. Beyond cancer, many chemicals cause multi-system damage, such as nervous system damage, birth defects and learning disabilities. Hormone-mimicking chemicals, such as dioxin, cause early puberty."

Some of us have six toes. Is this what you want to hear? We menstruate at eight. (I ate a fish and kept his chemicals). The older lungs wheeze beyond cancer. Hair is a painted luxury for some — more often wigs made from discarded mops.

Tire hammocks hang from every branch. Here we sleep, curled up in rubber bunks. Tonight the trees will squirm from the weight of our dreams. Our cradles will rock.
             Clickety — clickety — click. The peacock struts below.

We dream stories of a wooden horse. Bozeman and a pack of ponies. Galloping. One for each of us.

(Footnotes)
[1] All quotes are taken from the following: Trine, Cherie. "No Holnams Barred." Guest Editorial. *Rocky Mountain Bullhorn* March, 2001, which I happened to read while waiting for a slice of pizza. Something about the voice grabbed me, something I couldn't let get away.

Jacob Burd

Life In France

Then let it begin 13.0.0.0.0
godfuls of open mist
the split rivers of abortive hands
before we (all become paper targets
with necks worth 50 points

    1.   The water rails hungry and teaming
in the overlapping sentiments
the assaults of telegraph stops, paraphrase, abbreviation
rimmed against the greystone
like a storm of flesh
arms and legs, teeth beating through the whitecaps

    2.   At first taking the shoulder
in my palm, her shoulder
the interlude between the fine hairs
laying the elbow first

        that the whole body is vacuous
        the filling of the interlining gaps
        by the force of wanting

Fig. 1

the skin acceding and giving way
to thicken then to overlap   see Fig. 1

    2A. then this is the system and its variants
        (a) the god, the corresponding veintena within the introductory glyph
        (b) the time transpired since the above mentioned date

(c) the corresponding numeral-day
(d) the lord of the night
(e) the date of the lunar calendar
(f) the numeral month
(g) the event that occurred on that date
(h) the person who conducted the event
(i) his titles
(j) his place of residence and occasion
(h) his ascendance

3. at first I was alone
watching the storm through the window
the cold of its movement   see Fig. 2
the standstill of the roads
branches thrown off like night garments
and pinned to the chain link fences
I called you over

4. first we see the window
the storm
and then the lines of your face
tighten like triggers
follow the projective churning of the air
through the window and along your skin
a color like an electric current through the walls
        I am reminded of the vase we bought
        when the light comes through the concave
        ends of the glass and stops at the soles
            of your feet[1]
the lines that roll into blue

5. and instead of fragmenting

Fig. 2

---

[1] If train A runs daily at 6:00 AM to a point marked X and if three heartbeats can overlap in one wavelength to form a continuous hum, call it Y, then solve for

the rooms, each line enters the other
and enters from there
the room like the past enters breathing

6.   until their bodies rise
at us in the red of closed eyes
masticating in a sea of arms
and glimpsed profiles   see Fig. 3
the breasts of robins

Fig. 3

Fig. 4

7. a blue baby
then some are born with the fragility
seen in a quaking pupil
the shoulders of their body
carrying them out silently, cynical   see Fig. 4
or they are

8. if the light first joins
the water and falls back
and bounds through gestures that have
held a likeness of, say, a vase
or the parting of trees in the wind
a first kiss
or a bird aflight
      twisting its body over the river
      where the light passes through the tail feathers
      like a piece of blue glass

HILLCLIMB

Wayne Sheldrake

Free yourself from reality and you'll come back to it nonetheless.
—Debra Spark, *The Story Behind the Story*

If a cyclist who has survived open-heart surgery takes two-point-five milligrams of powerful anticoagulants on Sunday, Tuesday, Wednesday, Friday and Saturday, and five milligrams of powerful anticoagulants on Monday and Thursday decides to race his ten-speed up the highest paved road in North America, which begins at 7,540 feet above sea level and concludes at 14,130 feet above sea level, covers twenty-eight miles, and rises through seven atmospheres of barometric pressure, at what altitude and at what mile marker will his kidneys, liver, spleen, appendix, and heart explode? Please show your work with a graph.
—The author to himself, 7:29 a.m. July 24, 2004

When it snowed above 12, 000 feet July 23ʳᵈ, the day before the 2004 Bob Cook Memorial Mt. Evans Hillclimb, I had a plan. I bought a wet suit. I thought, *Those skinny boys, they will cry.* While those shiny-legged racers with three-percent body fat fight the freezer, I visualized myself cruising up the highest paved road in North America in a skin-tight womb of my own warm sweat. I actually took a test ride. Ever wonder what it's like to ride a bike in a wet suit? Wrap yourself in cellophane and swim laps in the Glenwood Hot Springs.

The plan falls through on race day. The morning is misty, not raining. It's cool, 47 degrees, goosebumpy in cycling shorts and a short sleeve jersey, but not cold enough to snow. My advantage as the only competitor with a wet suit is nullified.

I'm a little nervous about calling myself a bike racer. A friend of mine who really likes TV once asked me if I was a bicycle racer. I wasn't sure what to say. I ride my bike a lot, but I know bike racers. I know what they can do—things I couldn't do in my wildest *Breaking Away*-wet-suit-dreams.

"I guess it depends what you mean by racing," I answer.

"Do you pedal downhill?" he asks.

"Yeah, I pedal downhill."

"Anyone who pedals downhill is a bike racer in my book," he says, surfing from *Magnum* to CNN's latest Orange Alert.

I like his definition. Unfortunately, The Hillclimb, the only bike race I enter, doesn't have much downhill. It's decidedly uphill, twenty-eight miles from 7,450 feet to 14,130 feet. The last switchbacks of the mountain—steep, whipped gashes that scar the last five miles of the talus and tundra massif from 12,800 feet to the summit—conjure up the angles of spillways and escalators.

Information you need to know: I couldn't pass a high school sports physical, never did. I'm forty-four. At age thirty-three I survived open heart surgery for the implantation of a prosthetic aortic heart-valve. Fake heart valves, while miraculous, are not perfect. They're fake. To prevent blood from clotting like softballs on the plastic and titanium valve flaps, and keep the flaps from pitching stroke-inducing strikes into the catcher's mitt of your brain, anticoagulants are prescribed, for as long as you live. The drug, called Coumadin™, makes me a pharmaceutical hemophiliac. A nick shaving bleeds for half-an-hour. Small muscle tears most guys would walk off fill fast with my thinned blood forming clots that burn like internal blisters and persist for weeks. Think Barry Bonds whacking a few marbles into your calves with a cricket bat.

Also: The air above 12,000 feet is thinner than shirt-paper. Oxygen molecules are found about as often a fifty dollars bill in a dumpster. Not fun, if, like me, you have a fake heart valve *and* asthma.

I first "raced" Mt. Evans when I was forty. At the time I wrote:

Two hours and ten minutes into the race, a short sweeping descent carries me past Summit Lake to the feared switchbacks. At 13,000 feet I realize I have something in common with Bob Cook, Alexis Grewal, Jonathan Vaughters, and this year's winner Scott Moniger (who will finish more than an hour ahead of me).

No. Not speed — suffering. The difference? I suffer a lot longer.

For the last forty-five minutes, my body is wrapped in a tightening barbed-wire tourniquet. My arms feel like I am ski-jouring the Oregon Trail. My lungs feel like I have been snorting Krylon in "Megadeath Black." My eyeballs swim in a cocktail of jalapeno juice and jelly-fish venom. There's a rusty steak knife jabbed into my left kidney.

But my feet feel good. They're numb.

The last five miles, I averaged six miles per hour. Try that on flat ground. It's hard to *balance* a bike moving that slow.

I loved it.

The physical torture silences mental chit-chat. Thoughts retreat to blood. Sins hide in bone. Ambitions turn to breath and vanish into very thin air. You are not deep. You are not smart. You are not important. The effort requires everything valued as me-myself-and-I to get out of the way. Silent, small, self-reliant, quiet, wild indomitability rules. Afterwards I gobbled a peach, chugged a half-gallon of water, and puked. I wondered if I was holy, or had been for a little while.

Holiness aside, I liked the buzz, and I wanted to go back. There is no way to reproduce the tremulous rapture and the diplegiac aura of triumph found at the summit of the mountain except to go back, approach again, attack again, and know the overarching pain all that bliss sprouts from awaits.

A week before the race, two concerned friends told me about Gary, a robust, forty-year-old ex-jock. My friends said, "You know Gary is such an *animal*!" They said, "Gary — he's such an animal — he thinks he rode so hard on one of his bike rides that it triggered uncontrollable staph!" Within days Gary had been rushed to surgery, put on dialysis and a donor list. The conversation segues to warnings of another friend who claims Coumadin is killing her liver. I do my best to assuage their alarm, but I don't mention, Bob Cook, former Olympian who won the Mt Evans Hillclimb five times in a row (the race is now named for him). Sudden cancer attacked his brain after his victory in July of 1980 and he was gone by the spring. Could the strain of the race, that daunting altitude, be a trigger?

For my final training ride, I'd took two bottles of straight water and no food and peddled deep to a remote pass of the San Jauns. I hoped to work long enough to replicate the exhaustion of the Mt. Evans climb. The asthma kicked in, first a low swooping wheeze. The road hit sharp inclines. I stood to keep cranking. My lungs growled as if a hole had been ripped in my side with a Weedeater. Good. I needed to get used to that. Half hour later, my wife met me with the car near the top of an aspen cloaked curve at about 10,000 feet (not even half way up Evans). "You're an ANIMAL!" she hollered.

I decided not to tell her about Gary.

Race morning, I am not alone with my nerves. Just under 200 citizens herd under the "Start" banner ready to stab our handlebars at the belly of the Rockies. Almost all don professional looking Lycra in colors that would make the bumper of an '81 Subaru with Boulder plates proud. But even the guys who shave their legs, and the women who don't, look more like skiers, tennis players, or dart throwers than bike racers. The old guy to my left straddles a five thousand dollar bike with twelve hundred dollar rims. "Nice clip-ons," I say. "You too," he says. To my right is a quiet woman who, I will find out later, is the oldest woman in the event. She will win the 50-59 division with a ride of four hours and fifty two minutes.

"Do you pedal downhill?" I ask her.

"Yes, I do," she smiles.

In 1991, Lance Armstrong entered the Mt. Evans Hillclimb. He did not set a record. He did not win the race. This is one of the few bike races in the world where slugs like me, old guys in clip-ons, and grandmother quilters who pedal downhill can share the road with the likes of Lance, Olympic Gold Medalist Alexis Grewal, former record-holder on the mountain, or Mike Engleman, whose course record of one-hour fifty-four minutes stood for twelve years. The logistics of the long climb makes this possible. Citizens start at 7:30 in the morning. The pros and elite racers start at 8:15, followed in fifteen minute increments by waves of classified amateur and junior racers. By the time the big boys overlap citizens, we slugs are dispersed harmlessly, pedaling along as if the pavement were wet cement, as easy to avoid as roadkill.

From the start, I breathe like a landed trout. The race follows the winding cleave up Chicago Creek gorge, packed to its pine eaves with pellucid fog. I bustle behind bundles of passing bicycles searching for slipstreams. By the first mountainous twist of the road, I'm alone, straggling into mist the color of pocket lint. My tires feel flat. Cranks kick back like a dead Harley. Alpine chill wraps my body, a cold cast. My hands turn to stone. My chain oil turns to tar. I remember, *Temperatures drop 3-5 degrees for every 1,000 feet of elevation gained.* Alone, the cloudy highland is quiet. I peddle. Pain. Doubt. Pain. Doubt. Pain. Doubt.

Echo Lake, elevation 10,800, appears in an hour and seventeen minutes—a brief flat section. My wife hands me a windbreaker and neoprene gloves. *Halfway*, I want to think. But the next 3,330 feet loom out of sight above, fourteen zigzagging miles, twice as difficult as the previous fourteen.

At the east end of the lake the road enters a corridor into the Mt. Evans Wilderness. A pack of small children in rain ponchos gathered at a side-lot chant: DA-DDY! DA-DDY! DA-DDY!

"You have the nicest kids," the Forest Ranger at the entrance booth beams.

"Those aren't my kids," I gasp. But I love them anyway.

Into the wilderness, climbing out of and above the clouds now, I fall back on the meager talents of everyday life. I fight the urge to quit with stoicism: survival, though ignoble and unremarkable, though anonymous and agonizing, is at least survival. And in the most pitiable survival there is some truth, some—amidst the pain and doubt, pain and doubt, pain and doubt....

There's a short downhill at 12,800 feet, Summit Lake, then Escheresque ascensions beyond. Three miles from the finish, mountain goats share permafrost and foundered lichen-stone with a few sympathetic faces. At these lonely heights a strange face is as welcome as the ever-sparse oxygen. The encouragement of mittens clapping at the brittle air is better than the fifty dollar bill in a dumpster.

Throughout the race automobiles putter by, a race within a race. Drivers jockey to the top to meet riders too exhausted to risk the 7,000 foot, dry-ice descent. Somewhere my wife passes in a Subaru with a roof carrier that could be a sarcophagus. The cars swerving politely around my cocoon of suffering seem as irrelevant as a chairlift to a ski run.

I stand, my legs taffy-pulling. I row, my head drooping. Salt-stung vision blurs to fierce blue pixels. My lungs billow like Hefty bags head-locking a terrified rabbit.

Suddenly, on a switchback transplanted from a San Francisco hillside, I feel a push, a divine, miraculous hand at the base of my spine. I feel the rising my body and mind have been, for three hours, meanly denied. I could let go and gently fly. Oh. This is the explosion, the melt down of kidneys, liver, spleen, appendix, and heart bleeding beyond their walls. I've passed my last mile marker. I am *not* an animal. The buoyancy is amniotic, as exhilarating and fueling as it is disquieting and empty. I have no fear, no regret. The time is now, in the white heat of my foolish, fugue-ish high. *Relief. Death is....*

The hand belongs to my twenty-year-old nephew, one of those shiny-legged, skinny-boy racers who caught me from forty-five minutes behind. His arm cradles my back. I lean on him. He pushes me toward the ramping blue sky. I don't look over. I don't want him to see me cry. "You are a beautiful man," I whimper as he rides away. Two miles to go.

Eons later, I hear cheers from above. *Almost there!!* Angels.

The finish is a hooking switchback tight as a bank drive-up. That's it. The hot friction of internal torment stops. My burnt wick collapses into a puddle of cooling wax. Abruptly, myopic awareness blooms, and I am not alone. On a mat of chip-sealed pavement about the size of a McDonald's parking lot, from where, on a clear day, you can see Kansas and the troposphere, a hundred cyclists shake like Parkinson's victims circling a circus ring. We unclench fists to operate brakes. Bikes are dropped. Blankets grabbed. The windows of our hearts are wide open and at 14,000 feet the wind blowing in is frickin' freezing.

The day after: I'm tracing paper. One wrong move from the tub to the towel rack and muscle fibers will burst like drought-dried cattails banging barbed-wire fence in a lightning storm. My thoughts manage only the brittle ephemera of gray erasable-bond tapped through an antique, mite-nibbled ribbon. I've been flayed to the pink and thrown down, bones minced. Every wicker of me seems unmeshed.

The pain of the ride, so slowly extruded from me, like screws dipped in dry ice, is forgotten. It must be that when we are soft and pliable, defenseless and spent, pain works its way undetectably back into our marrow — a waterborne parasite to lie dormant with its zealous, secret kind until the bars of our emotional zoo drop, the wildness spills, and reintroduction is inevitable. That's why we go out again and do something, quickly, to wring the pain out with our *own* hands and legs before some asshole, without warning, turns the screw-heads for us and the hidden tenderness comes twisting out as anger, as fear, as unrequited suicidal love.

Such thoughts I've lost — left amidst the bighorn, the pika, the bristlecones (How could I have forgotten them?), and the white skirts of the goats. Yesterday's Eureka's evaporated. Final, satisfying solutions every one. Alas.

But, ascending slowly above ash-colored clouds on half-a-helix of black-top warped and waved like a funhouse mirror, chucked with yellow-bellied marmot holes, and lumped with tundra, I forget, almost completely, my flawed heart, and I remembered why — why I keep coming back again and again, older and older, slower and slower, one last time. I come to remind myself of, if not *The* truth, *some* truth — the truth of my tiny struggle: the toughest, touchable, most laughable, too easily forgotten truth.

Jefferson Navicky

Snow

The car
rolled over
somewhere in Connecticut,

her forehead cut,
her thighs.

Sitting on a snow bank,
face and hands
a silent band of red, and black
like a wide night color
forced upon her.

Morgan Reitmeyer

Cycles of this Heart

She throbs in a **relentless** circle,
      loops **weaving** into incomprehensible patterns,
          deeply recognizable.

    spinning tops.
    ancient dervishes.
    eddies **in time**, repeating ourselves over and over again,
broken records of **living** moments.

        It is said that a fish has a memory of **seconds**,
            and therefore each **turn** in the same bowl appears to be
      a new place,
        a discovery.

There is no learning in this.
    Flesh bound **memories** vary;
      some **shorter** than the koi,
      some longer than we want.

Humans are a **terrible** history of curves,
    black on red on **war**,
      genocide on **dusty** ground.

all the art **made**,
all the ideas mulled **over**.
We live in **myths** of progress, a sham of li(n)es and upward/heavenward mobility.

I stood beneath a goddess not too long ago. She leaned over offerings of sweet smoke and oranges, and looked at me for a time. It was my turn to draw a lot from her pile, and she asked me if I recognized her. My hair fell in front of my face; yes, I know you mother. You appear in every culture, you wear the dress of stars that shows sailors the way home, and you are the cool breezes that bring crops to fullness. She smiled in the corner of her mouth; you know nothing, **all this time and you know next to nothing**. I drew. She laughed in a crow's voice, a waterfall sound, as I hurried to collect my fortune.

There is you, curling in my chest like a **lost** dream.
        I have been everywhere with you, to the end.
            I recognize this sinking **feeling**.
I know it is you peeling the skin off **my heart**,
razor precision, cutting in, slicing yourself in.
        This time, with a practiced eye, I can **see** my hand wielding the scalpel.

I want to say a **spiral**.
That we are truly **creatures** that see when we look,
can **make choices** and let them play out,
we are not trapped?

Stand back further and see what is **constant**.

Stand back further still and see it as an **illusion**.

Each isolated mote of life penetrates our handcrafted worlds, leaving echoes of reality in us, the clay of my soul humming in a new pitch **after encountering that slow sigh**, singing with a new voice after I breathe in the cold morning after.

I know enough **to be afraid** now,
to know it is fear that **will kill me**,

        I put a thin cage around **my** heart.
Under that **artful** scarring is something
designed to explicitly keep my own shape when encountering the fierce **heat** of you.
        Wires hold me together, an intricate knot work of symbols and **memories**.
            You may encounter them as **we cut** at my flesh.

It is made **for** both our protection;

        a: You will be allowed to find the **freedom** that you need
                without being bogged down in tearful chunks of muscle.

        b: I will be able to remember who I am when **I look** at you.

This mesh of me, this can be formed;
I **refuse** to be ridged,
        but I refuse to be watered down,
                forced to go through a tedious distillation process to recover my essence.
I am trying **to step out of** that lost cycle,
        the time when
        I
lose **my**
             rhythm in
                        the ocean
        beating of the world
I may be stumbling into
some other   well   worn   path,
a **road** tamped down by a million others.
It **is impossible** that I am not.

when I let myself forget,
it's new to me.
Maybe there is learning here.

The next three hours are largely lost in a pain haze, pushing my heavy bike over the leg-breaking hills between Carter Lake, Masonville, and Fort Collins. These are my home roads. I know the texture of the pavement in my seat and in my palms.

On a good day, unladen, I can average around 18mph over these hills with some effort. This time, I hit six miles an hour.

Trevor Even

Eleven Dollar Minimum

Slick black metal and shiny silver trim, *and it rocks like a baby on potholes. (Go to sleep.) Brakes, brakes. Not enough brakes. Where are the cigarettes? Green light. Yellow. Go faster.*

An alien tree in a drought-wracked avenue island stands half dead and bare between the rows of anonymous masses. Nobody looks. What's to see? Nothing but space dead and gone as the blast of the gas hits the black and the light turns from bright red to green. Nothing but what comes between where I was leaving and the place I now have to be. The sun sets to fire feathered clouds and the warping of light summons color from what was once white and grey. The light glares in your glasses. Phoenix's glint wreathing masses of life could leave you blind, maybe spread like vomit over yards of hot afternoon pavement. It's better if you just keep your head out of the clouds.

Where am I going?

Swaths of undeveloped land slash inconspicuously by. Weeds, grass, ants, birds, cacti blow in the wind, get ate by machines. It really has no meaning for us. Wind's a sting in our eyes and a burn on our skin, scattering papers, ripping signs, sending power lines, trees onto family filled metal boxes. Nothing but trouble from *wind*. Blowing in the wind leads to standing in the rain and reduced visibility. Visibility is important. Keep the clouds off of your head.

Slickness and sliding and flowing about are the things foisted upon us—on the floors of dirty kitchens; the ooze from our skin when a sharpness stops being abstract. Ours is a world where the things that slide 'round often do so at one tenth the sound of speed, with the force of firebombs full of razors, the bone wrench of hot steel and screeching. Keep your motherfucking head out of fractals. Remain within the parallel lines. Shit.

Turn around, read the sign. Can't read the fucking sign. Glasses fell; take the right. Styrofoam squeaks; music plays. Smoke disappears, reappears, fades like the fog as it nears you.

We do not relish the compulsion to move, get up, *dodge*. (Only after the act is it pleasurable.) Understandable of course, but a shame. Especially when so many things seem sent from sprawling nowhere, crash down right into our hearts, leave everything burnt to black and char. All the words, all the signs, all the mumbling on the edges of bars and shadowed corridors bouncing between satellites, the terminal velocity of near frictionless forms raining down on our heads and our backs; if we inadvertently started memorizing the paths of the brace-beggared things under gravity's cold dead pull, we'd probably catch more in our eyes than we thought. Damn right, keep your head out of the clouds. Keep looking up and you just might get vertigo.

Brick house, four kids. Bouncing rubber balls in growing synch. Thump, thump, thumpthump. "Let's all bounce at the exact same time." Hi. 14.76. Two dollar tip. See ya, kids.

The meal manifests and the family hangs in its place; I slide off their slab and start pulling a thread back to center. Trace my lines on a wall and it's a schizophrenic's spider web, hanging off of the guts of the fed, off of those who avoid or fail at the nightly repast's preparation. The more we eat the more thread hangs — the socially dead bodies of the hungry pile up, new walls for the thread to hang off (the first few tips usually pay for the gas; increased business means a couple more drivers). Not that I'm not trapped, too. A metaphor's hunger for organs is a damnable thing to escape. The garbage goes into the dumpster, piles up like dead dogs, way out in the back near the gas lines; the city eats on, in convenience. We are all of us being digested, gobbled up 'fore our eyelids first cracked. All we see are our respectively nervous and grease-sheened young faces, staring, smiling 'cross dilated doors. Convenient, I guess, since I doubt this thing would much tolerate looks in the eye. It's like I said — keep your head in two dimensions at a time. There isn't a wizard. There isn't a curtain. Keep on eating. Keep it down. Keep it real. How's it going?

Please insert coin to continue. Simple enough for small children.

("Food for people, age 5-100.")

Have a nice day, afternoon, and/or night.

No awkward pauses in a society where nobody speaks. Proximity never demands any sort of exchange — the TV is quite the orator, gives us both something to hear. The nightmare is, the talk of the town ends up telling the town how to talk, ("Current conditions outside: partly cloudy and warm") as if we've nothing to say when it comes to the state of our world.

Walking the streets is for hippies and anarchist punks, the hobos that sleep in the dumpster — you gotta keep your head out of the things that dictate the state of your environment. On those little slips of paper; on the screen the nation speaks for us, and Mother takes in all the weeping and silent the same. What's happening? Nothing. *We just live here, man.* Everything already has happened. It doesn't come from anywhere. Not from anyone else — it's just there. Message from God, in God's country (Don't look up: you'll go blind from the shock — the greatest in the history of the Earth). Car. Game on. Donkey punch. Remember, the spider suspends us all.

Overweight girl with a giant styrofoam wizard's head stands at the corner and holds up a sign. "Exciting new rental community." Raccoon on the roadside bloats into an upside down coffee table. The crows are too smart to dig in.

Hmm.

We're really just not used to this. Things are supposed to work, after all, a bit like a demolition derby. You know? On a fundamental level of mutual trust — no rules, at least, not really; more efficient and effective the more the little players knock around. The problem comes when someone gets the notion that maybe the game needs a winner, or that it's time for the drunken announcer to call in the giant mechanical monster, wrap everything up with slaughter. It's simply safer to stay in the stands — anywhere where the creeping monstrosity cannot hit you with its mind-cracking mass. Where it cannot put you in the position of having no choice but to raise up your eyes in a moment of unexpected seriousness.

This may be why we don't like looking up. Generations ago the monster came a'crashing through the bleachers, and all of us ran, swearing to our hearts to never again unpeel them with the horror of its vision. Keep yourself chained to easily communicable perceptions. (Pretend what is easily communicated always contains a perception!) *Y'all don't go too far now.* Keep your head out of the blossom of looming explosion!

Don't look at how the pile of corpses grows. Flesh falls off bones by the minute. Minds go out to lunch, get kidnapped in the parking lot, raped, chopped up, and dumped in the previously garbage-free patch of woods. Worlds erupt in fire and the children hold up empty hands, trembling from long years of hunger and drinking poisoned water. The screens blink out horror from places where our nylon-swathed feet never fall, and the screens are a'blinking it all. Keep your head out of the clouds. Speak you only those things you've heard of. Never again shall we speak of the gods and the crackling bolts they fling.

This is a country founded on rational thinking.

Giant goddamn white behemoth frothing at the bug catcher, slops like a drunk bum's drool into the lane my little car slides through. Honk, startle, eyes pop like pimples wide open and white. The machine chokes down more gas. The driver wants to get away as fast as his car possibly can. (That place always creeps him out. It's where he almost crashed into a little multicolored car ten seconds ago.)

I think somebody went for the win. In fact, I get the impression they're still trying to get it, right now. You sure as hell can't trust *words* anymore. They will snap your ass right up, and carry you off by the neck. Or, should the hoarding urge fail, just beat you down and explain away the breaking of your bones as if such things were but shudders in the fundaments of life, long forgotten.

If you speak another language, falteringly, glancing at meanings each time you push out a sound, you'll notice a new taste in your mouth when you slide back to the tongues of your mother and father. You realize just how much you keep your eyes closed — it's a bit like being in a relationship founded on silent bonds of mutual alcoholism after half of your pair sobers up. So much is just hollow, clinking bottles of dark black glass whose weight casts a glimmer on the inside. You speak, you assume there is some substance. Very rarely is it actually there. Only when you pick up a full one do you notice you've got no meaning to drink of.

At least, not the sort of meaning a word usually has…

Like REAL. "1. existing; not imaginary; actual." You grow up and think it's this one. You get told it, by wary elders, when you stumble and fall into screens. When you ponder at too late an age towards futures of heroes and wonders. When you shiver from ghosts creeping up closet doors as the trucks pass by your bedroom window. "2. genuine; true; authentic." You think it's this one when you're stupidly wandering around in halls filled with slim metal boxes, cold metal locks, and teachers with wet, doughy flesh. Want to be it, want to have it, wonder how much it costs, hate everyone around you who thinks they got it already last week. In the end, it usually comes down to this one, the last one in the little orange book: "3. of property; movable; as lands." From a thing to bring center, a thing to lust for — in the end, it's a thing done to you. It takes over, one day, all the world.

The meaning, rolling right off of the hazardous chemical shelves, is what gives the word its use in the first place. You think the world to be the first when it's actually the third, loathing the *real* world for every cent its worth. You decide to spend every dime on the imaginary, on the buffers, on the lies (everyone simply forgot what imaginary things *really* look like). The spider continues to feed, the robot continues to demolish the ancient and helpless. The game, however, goes on far away from our minds. Or it continues in our memory; in memory forever. Even if we all forget it.

Nice trick.

The clouds might be nice, but they're *real*—who the fuck wants to look at this mess?

A handful of hours eat up the whole day. Moments of searing pain kept silent burn away all they once called companions. Contort, contract, catch a corner of steel in the temple, slide a thin latex glove over a sliced-open finger because the boss ran out of band-aids last week. Watch as the blood fills the synthetic skin, dries dark brown in the cracks of your knuckles. This is the world of our labor. This is the world we call *real*. I suppose it's as real as it gets.

Cars like containers in a long-dead warehouse sit cool and reflective in the towering parking lot lamps; the girls from the nail shop fumble with their keys after a day of grinding grime out of upper-middle class cuticles. The twilight sky sinks to a drab bluish gray, and the clouds of the day spread and drift, slide away, making room for the thunderheads that come with the dawn, perched on the mountains like dragons settling down on phone lines. Stop, keys, door, throw the cigarette, back inside. Dishes in a pile like pick up sticks. Gonna fall.

Heather Martin

Pathway of the Waves

The phone rang just before three. My father's voice scratched across the line, each word followed by a dry crack—a still-spinning record after playing the last song. He called me Maureen, as if "go to your room" were to follow.

I numbly packed a bag, barely able to discern blacks from navies in the shadowy closet light. I hadn't done laundry in weeks, so my choices were limited. I pulled a balled black satin blouse out of the hamper and tossed it in the bag. Mr. Coffee choked and sputtered the final drops into the carafe, which I transferred to my travel-mug. Flying home was not an option. With $8.15 frozen in my checking account, and no forthcoming offers from home, a solitary drive was the only choice.

I left shortly after 4 AM.

The sun eclipsed the road before me as I drove east. I sipped coffee and smoked, watched the first sober sunrise I could remember. The pavement stretched in front of me, a wayward vein across the continent—my progress, a few dotted lines across an imagined map.

At the first gas station, I realized that I had left my license in my apartment. It was likely on the bedroom floor in the front pocket of the jeans I wore out two nights before. Clumsy and forgetful at the bar, I avoided carrying a purse by pocketing my ID and cash. Luckily, I had my wallet and credit cards. If I were without them, I would have been stranded, out of gas, no money, and no identification. Maybe I *could* have started a new life there in the tiny border-town so aptly named, Kanorado.

Back on the road with a fresh pail of sweetened coffee, I felt good. Guilty, but good. I was in no hurry to reach my destination. The endlessness and anonymity of the highway was comforting—more so than Aunt Sherry waiting with her chocolate "Congo" bars and coffee-milk.

The fields of sunflowers and wheat, the scattered grazing cows, the pink sky, parted by the road and my little blue four-door, all converged behind me leaving no trail, no evidence of my ever having been there. I rode in silence. The engine clicked and hummed through cities and towns, my limbs tingling with caffeine and latent anticipation. Thoughts escaped my control, zooming back and forth, as if the road were a curving timeline to smoothly traverse, one image thinly connected to the next.

...Topeka...

I thought of her and of Dad and of them together. Her thin blond hair, parted down the middle, lifting and then flopping against her forehead with the weight of the wind. Dad, with one finger on the wheel, glancing at her across the seat, or flexing his toes, a foot hung out of the driver-side window.

...St. Louis...

She, positioned squarely on hands and knees in the backyard garden framed with old railroad ties, tugged and dug and grinned under the shade of an oversized Stetson amongst the tall tomato plants. "You need to crack the nut before you can eat the kernel," she said to me with her fingers into the soil. I poked a finger into the dirt and removed it, examining the brown line beneath my fingernail. Dad looked on from the porch, shirtless in jeans, resting a jug of soon-to-be sun tea on the weathered railing. She brushed a wayward blond strand from her eye, left a stripe of soil on sun-pinked cheek.

...Indianapolis...

A stripe of blood slipped across pale cheek after she was attacked during a morning jog. Her body trembled. Dad paced across green shag. I stretched my arms around her midsection, rested my head on the low lump of her belly, listened for a message from the tiny body within; would it still come? It never came. Later though, Dale did. A purple blob, eyes closed, kicking his right foot over and over in the incubator. The foot grew and found its place in my back, stomach, legs. Dale. A stumbling, tumbling, yellow-haired torrent of teeth and nails. Cutting figure-eights across the blacktopped driveway on an orange Bigwheel, a paper plate decorated with spray-painted ziti strung around his neck. I sat, balled on the stoop, knees to nose, listening to the rumbling sound of plastic on tar. The wind lifted the plate to smack against his ear.

...Columbus...

A smack across the neck, her hand meant for my cheek. Bitch, I had said. Surly and strong, hand clipped to my hip: defiant, disinterested. I cut my eyes and dared her. She looked fierce — and tired. A ripple of loose skin hung like a tear from her chin. The partial palm-print — alive with heat — was later soothed with ointment from her fingertip.

...Pittsburgh...

Fingertips on flesh; probing, pulling, tearing. The TV laugh-track dully flicked behind the hissing in my ears. Was this love? The acrid stench and burn of fucking behind a couch. Three quick blasts of the horn; finger tapping as she waited for me outside in a parked car. The quiet ride home. Fun time? Yes. She hummed, adjusted the air vents. I stared out the window, aware of the dull throbbing between my legs.

A red light on my dashboard glowed, signaling the car's need for fuel. I pulled off the interstate, unaware of my town or city or state. The sun shone high in the sky, marked a sleek shadow behind me. A section of hair blew into my mouth as I yawned. After watching the pump's white number dial roll back on itself, I walked inside, on legs rubbery and unsure. The diamond-shaped woman behind the counter squinted at me suspiciously, swiped my credit card for gas, cigarettes, coffee. The shoulder of her orange Gas-N-Go uniform was torn, revealing a grayed bra strap. She caught me looking.

In the white light of the bathroom, my reflection was an unflattering smattering of purples and reds, underlain with greenish-white. I twisted my hair into a greasy brown bun on the top my head, accentuating the deep crescents cut below my eyes. I had a momentary urge to vomit, but swallowed it back not wanting to clutch the cracked and shit-stained unisex toilet visible behind me in the mirror.

In the car again, I rolled the window down, the warm afternoon breeze fell in puffs against my forehead. The lack of sleep was taking its toll. Intermittent body quakes and slippery palms on the wheel were evidence of my steady intake of coffee and cigarettes. The car drifted across into the left lane. I was aware of it, but unable to prevent the little car's sway. A horn whined, and a yellow pick-up rocketed past my window, the driver yelling something unintelligible, shaking a fist in my direction. Not wanting to eat or sleep, I pulled off the highway to compose myself.

I exited at a rest area peppered with port-a-potties and picnic tables. A white-haired man was jerked behind a leashed dog covered in knotted thickets of wool. The dog stopped to urinate; the man scratched his armpit. The two then disappeared behind a mammoth motor home parked horizontally across several blue-lined spaces. I pulled the lever at the base of my seat, sliding into a reclining position, folded my elbow across my eyes.

When I awoke, it was dark.

Outside the window stood a young woman, fingers curled around a payphone receiver. She massaged her temples with the other hand, her hair spilling across her fingers, covering her face. She leaned into the half-enclosed booth. Her body shook with what might have been laughter or sobs.

Dale and I sat in the back, confused. No one had explained why we were no longer continuing south; why they had stopped singing along with the radio; why she pulled on her ponytail and he sped recklessly. She passed back some Colorforms for Dale to stick on the window and a dog-eared children's magazine for me to read. We pulled off at a rest stop and she stood outside the car at a payphone. She let the receiver drop from her hand and fell against the Plexiglas booth. "However long the day," I heard her say as he climbed out the car, "the night must fall."

"I know." he said and gripped her tight.

When I looked again, the woman at the payphone was gone. The receiver swayed in the wind. I opened the car door, gagged and vomited coffee on the pavement, drove back onto the highway. The night bled into the morning and the morning into the afternoon. The color of the trees ran together, dizzying to eye one from the rest. These fragments of memory raced and slowed, tumbled on top of each other, traversing the terrain of our lives together. Moments long forgotten pushed their way to the surface blurring my eyes. I was nearing the end of my journey, my journey home.

...Baltimore...

We packed the old station wagon until it creaked and crunched under the weight, drove through the night, and woke to the customary greeting, "Mornin'," when we entered one of the diners dotting the interstate for a hot and greasy breakfast. We giggled and even laughed out loud when our waitress shouted our orders across the counter to the fry cook. The pancakes, doughy and sticky. She and I split a side order of hash browns with ketchup.

The name of my town started appearing in white letters on the road signs before me. The distance shrunk from hundreds of miles to tens. Off the highway, familiar landmarks were buried by the shiny lights and plastic of new businesses familiar only in name. The trip, five years past due, was over.

home.

I set my chin on the back of the front seat and listened to her whisper to me as she drove — the thickness of the southern air damp on our skin. Dad and Dale slept in their seats. She asked me questions, talked to me about important things. She held my hand and squeezed it — a reminder that she was there.

Home. My father was sitting on the porch when I arrived. A grey figure. He tapped his pointer finger on the arm of the rocker. He looked up, surprised to see me. "The night must fall, Maura," he said.

"I know," I said.

David Gruber

Livre Melancholique

"The sea was close today but I did not touch her"
– Robert Kelly

As it is always.
Only gulls arrive to explain
In the meditations there work
Tuneless harmonies.

We called that river home,
Or so I believed, hearing echoes from
Cars across the bridge,
The one high up or the other, low against

The water; how many who have crossed
Stopped once, peering at some discarded plum.
Here is not the same,
There are no shadows yet to follow.

I saw a stump lie half-drowned
In long grass, adrift. And
Three generations in a corner cemetery,
Their farm a trailer park.

The sea was close, yes, but
Her face was dark, I avoided her unmirroring.
She tapped her foot, hummed.
The rim of a wheel across a bridge

MATTER
literature.art.movement

NOW ACCEPTING
SUBMISSIONS
DUE 01 FEB 2005

Lacunae:

Empty Space, Fabric of Landscape,
Discontinuity, Future Primitive,
Arbitrary Attachments,
Ecological Infatuations

Fiction: 7500 words
Non-Fiction: 7500 words
Poetry: Five Poems
Maps, Schematics,
Photography,
Visual Art & Design
Inquire for details at:
www.matterjournal.com

Send submissions to:

MATTER
PO BOX 814
Fort Collins, CO 80522

Spring 2005
ISSUE No. 6

"Think of bicycles as rideable art that can just about save the world."

-grant petersen

Bicycle: The History

a review.

an excerpt.

an interview with author
david v. herlihy.

Evan P. Schneider

Velocipedes, Bone Shakers, and High Wheels: The Road to the Modern Bicycle

"To the velocipede, gentleman, that ingenious and charming machine, by now a faithful friend and inseparable companion to the solitary and wary traveler. To that useful invention, bequeathed by science to a stunned and grateful world. Yes, gentleman, let us drink to this carriage of the future. To its perfection, to its success, and to its long and useful existence."
–Toast at a cycling banquet, 1868

As it turns out, history can be a daunting and slippery thing to document. Perhaps that's why David V. Herlihy spent years holed up in libraries around the world researching key figures in the innovation of various machines that would eventually morph into the modern-day bicycle. In what is being hailed as "the definitive account of the two-wheeler," Herlihy beautifully explains what he gathered from several trips throughout the U.S. and Europe and organized his fantastic findings into a 400-plus-page spectacle of specifics in *Bicycle: The History*.

Bicycle is certainly a must-read for anyone who takes bikes apart for fun, participates in training rides or races, harbors philosophical or emotional connections to pedaling, or commonly commutes around town on a bike. If it doesn't exponentially enhance your knowledge of the bicycle's tumultuous past, Herlihy's history will bring you to a jaw-dropping appreciation of the machine that took over 100 years to come close to perfection. We might take its product for granted, but the bicycle's past is full of patent battles, public ridicule, marketing brilliance, and technological prowess.

Whereas most available histories of the pedal-powered two-wheeler begin around 1875, about the time the high-wheel bicycle (seat mounted precariously above a humungous front wheel) became all the rage, Herlihy roams back some hundred years prior to the ill-fated yet fundamentally important four-wheeled carriages, draisines, and velocipedes (average sized wheels with a seat between them without chains, brakes, or pedals, pushed by the rider's kicking legs). When you finally read about the first practical rear-wheel, chain-driven bicycle, you are ecstatic—at last, something you recognize, the mystery solved—the bicycle as we know it having come to fruition and into production after about fifty years of toiling, wrecking, and rebuilding.

Even if Herlihy presents it matter-of-factly, we have been waiting for the revelation for nearly half the book. Everyone dabbling in bicycle production in the mid 1880s agreed only one idea was lacking (the chain, you want to scream into the pages, the CHAIN!) to get the bicycle truly right; the book becomes an entangling drama, exciting to watch unfold. Since we know now what technicians didn't know then, the tension is excruciating. As the author capitalizes on, "the mechanical marvel we know today as the bicycle was actually the culmination of a long and elusive quest for a human-powered vehicle, a remarkable story that has yet to be told in full detail."

Presented chronologically while flip-flopping sides of the Atlantic, several interesting extra insets dot *Bicycle*, adding color to the, while informative, sometimes monochrome fact-repeating and record-reporting prose. Both facts and funnies are pertinent in a definitive look at the bicycle and Herlihy lays them out so well that what could easily be a droning textbook becomes a lively, often humorous and always intriguing narrative. The inset "High-Wheel Accessories," for example, lists the possible accoutrements available for prospective buyers in the 1880s, such as warning bells, horns, cyclometers, oil-based hub lamps, and woolen suits with matching caps. But Herlihy hardly stops there. Included are side notes on "Amateurs vs. Professionals," "Extreme Indoor Racing," "Importance of Bearings," "Racial Restrictions," "Women and the Velocipede," "A Military Bid," "Specialized Services" (like couriers), "The Motorcycle Spin-off" and several others.

One of the most fascinating incorporations in *Bicycle* is the sheer number of engravings, drawings, photographs, and promotional posters it boasts between its lines. Someone wanting a rather solid knowledge of the bicycle's past could do far worse than meandering through the pictures Herlihy has dug up.

It's really in the laymen-friendly explanations, though, that *Bicycle* takes its highest honors. Not only is the book all-inclusive, but it's accessible, thorough, and genuinely enjoyable. In the end, when full-suspension Cannondales populate the pages and people all over the world have come to know the convenience of a relatively simple human-powered machine, it's easy to miss the people who got things rolling. Thanks to Herlihy, though, the bicycle and its pioneers may finally be seen as very real yet latent catalysts to the production of roads, aviation, and even perhaps the women's rights movement.

Bicycle: The History is nothing less than superb. Herlihy shows precisely how important the bicycle was in historically challenging and changing people's lifestyle, from exercise to fashion. Herlihy reminds us, as Stephen Crane so simplistically put it: "Bicycle is everything."

1907 J.W. GRADY NEW ENGLAND SPECIAL RACER

David V. Herlihy

An excerpt from *Bicycle: The History*

In spite of the popularity of city-sponsored races, not all observers lent their approval. Some citizens decried the road closures that were enforced on race days. One grouch in Fontainebleau chastised the city for spending its scarce resources on race decorations. Some officials even refused to sanction the events. When a bicycle maker in Clermont-Ferrand proposed races in conjunction with a musical festival planned for the spring of 1869, the mayor withheld his support. He insisted that the program schedule was already full, nor would the budget allow for any prizes.

Races were also plagued by frequent logistical and technical mishaps. On several occasions, unruly crowds invaded the field, causing delays, accidents, and cancellations. And even when unmolested, the riders often faltered on their own, by misplacing their feet on the pedals or failing to make a turn. With alarming regularity they fell, usually taking down others in the process. Longer races over regular roads were particularly problematic. The winner of one eight-mile run in Le Neubourg, Normandy, arrived in less than an hour, but four of the twelve entrants failed to finish.

Still, these contests gave mechanics a valuable opportunity to test new products and gradually improve the machine. Many programs also included exhibitions where bicycle makers could display and sell their products, while providing a fruitful forum for the exchange of technical ideas. To further encourage development, sometimes a jury would award prizes to the best machines and accessories. To be sure, the racers themselves were not always receptive to promising propositions. They spurned, for example, a nifty freewheel mechanism by A. Boeuf of Tarare, no doubt out of fear that device would add needless complexity. Like the Dexter hub previously introduced in the United States, this mechanism would have enabled them to adjust their pedaling cadence at will, while the front wheel spun on its own accord.

Nevertheless, racers widely adopted at least one critical improvement in the course of 1869: the inch-thick solid rubber tire designed to give a more comfortable ride than the standard iron variety. Initially proposed by Clément Ader, a future aviation pioneer, the idea was slow to catch on. Even *Vélocipède Illustré* at first dismissed rubber tires as an impractical luxury, likely to wear out quickly or even fall off the rims to which they were crudely attached with wire strands or rivets. But bicycle makers soon introduced metal rims with U- and V-shaped cross-sections that allowed tires to be securely cemented or wedged into place. Racers quickly proved that these tires were not only durable and comfortable, they also increased speed. Soon tourists adopted them as well, and they became standard accessories on all varieties of cycles.

Racers also began to adopt larger front wheels so that the bicycle would go farther with every revolution of the cranks. The large driving wheel, however, created a flap on the racing circuit. Some organizers banned bicycles with wheels exceeding thirty-eight inches to ensure that the contests hinged on superior skill rather than equipment. Proponents of the bigger wheel, however, claimed that such restrictions impeded technical progress. The issue boiled over at a race in Marennes. A competitor from nearby Rochefort showed up with an objectionably large front wheel, prompting the local competitors to storm off the field in protest. Eventually, organizers resolved the matter by restricting the wheel size in some events while leaving others open-ended. This policy effectively forced the dominant Parisian professionals to compete among themselves, mercifully saving the local competitors from certain embarrassment.

By the fall of 1869, the bicycle's novelty value was starting to wear thin. Many wealthy individuals who had once indulged in the fashion were no longer active riders, and many specialized firms had already folded. Still, there were some encouraging signs. Races, though fewer, still drew large crowds, and affirmed that the velocipede was making steady technical progress. There were even indications that the elevated price of a good machine would soon descend to a more affordable level. One maker in Clermond-Ferrand, who advertised his velocipedes at 225 francs in May, listed them at 150 francs by September, proudly announcing that he had "finally resolved the problem of how to bring the velocipede within the public's means."

Bicycle: The History

Interview with David V. Herlihy

Matter: Years of research and scholarly determination undoubtedly went into the writing of Bicycle: The History. Once a member of the Harvard Cycling Club, what prompted you to delve so deeply into the often-convoluted details surrounding the bicycle's history and write this book?

Herlihy: You might say that I was drawn into bicycle history when I stumbled on a basic but intriguing question—who put the pedals on the obsolete kick-propelled two-wheeler and thus triggered a veritable revolution in transportation? As I began researching the matter in France I met Jacques Seray, who had just written a coffee-table book on bicycle history. He told me derailleurs weren't nearly as interesting as the pioneer period, which surprised me since I thought I was already doing ancient history. When he learned that I was from Boston, he pointed to a haunting photo in his book showing a proud young man perched on a "boneshaker"—the first primitive bicycle of the 1860s. Seray told me that this obscure individual named Pierre Lallement had claimed the world's first bicycle patent in America, but he wound up buried in a pauper's grave in Boston in 1891 at the start of the great bicycle boom. Seray explained that Lallement's story was steeped in mystery, and that his actual role in launching the original bicycle company, Michaux of Paris, was never truly settled. His own take led me to believe that Lallement was something more than the marginal imposter portrayed in most post-boom histories. Having never heard of Lallement, I was stunned to think that a genuine bicycle pioneer might be buried in Boston unbeknownst to the public. And then I learned that this was but one of several intriguing questions pertaining to early bicycle development which really hadn't been resolved over the years. The list includes the precise contribution of the German baron Karl von Drais, creator of the original kick-propelled two-wheeler of 1817, and the role of the Olivier brothers of Paris, wealthy entrepreneurs who hid in the shadows of Michaux. Finding out that there is a small international circle of scholars who care deeply about bicycle history and meet annually gave me further incentive to delve deeper and to eventually write up my findings.

Matter: Given the imminent oil crisis, does the United States stand on the brink of another bicycle renaissance/revolution/boom? You quote a writer in 1892 who stated that "The effect [of bicycles] upon the development of cities will be nothing short of revolutionary." Can this still hold true?

Herlihy: I think in some sense that writer has already been vindicated—certainly the commuter bicycle is a ubiquitous sight in countless cities around the world today and likely to remain so for some time to come. But there's no question that we Americans could make far better use of the bicycle as a practical means of transportation than we do now, especially in major cities where traffic is increasingly congested. The net savings of oil could be substantial, not to mention other tangible payoffs like a cleaner and friendly environment. So I think the potential is still there for another "revolution in locomotion" (as the *New York Times Paris* correspondent described the bicycle outlook in 1867). Of course, the bicycle is not the only alternative to the automobile for urban transportation, but it remains one of the most sensible and compelling means to save time and money in transit, while getting a good workout to boot.

Matter: Recently, several American cyclists have gained popular recognition for their accomplishments in major road races. Will this collective success do anything to raise sympathy for modern velocipedists who often complain that automobile drivers have no patience or understanding for sharing the road with bicycles?

Herlihy: The bicycle's competitive and utilitarian sides are really quite distinct. You're not likely to find Lance Armstrong or his colleagues biking to the supermarket or cinema. And I suspect that very few races spontaneously erupt among cycle-commuters. Still, I think it's likely that as Americans develop a greater appreciation for the competitive sport they will become, at the very least, more tolerant of those who use bicycles simply to get around. In France and Italy, where the sport has long been popular, motorists generally seem more considerate of cyclists on the road, whether out for a ride or trying to get somewhere. I think that's likely the result of a widespread appreciation for the bicycle in all its forms.

Matter: Europe has been considered more cycling-conscious than the USA for a few decades. Why have we strayed so far from a pastime that, according to your book, had been responsible for so much of what we enjoy today, such as car production and highway systems, while Europeans are still connoisseurs and dilettantes of the bicycle?

Herlihy: That's a difficult question to answer. At several intervals Americans have shown an enthusiasm for the bicycle that was at least comparable to that of their European contemporaries—the "boneshaker" craze of the late 1860s, the boom of the 1890s, and the revivals of the 1930s and 1970s. But it is also true that, in contrast with Europeans, Americans have repeatedly failed to sustain a strong level of commitment to cycling. In the aftermath of the great boom, for example, the wealthier classes lost all interest in the recreational sport. The competitive sport, meanwhile, failed to give the struggling industry a significant boost. The public still took an interest in track racing through the 1930s, but the failure to establish a road-racing tradition on a par with the Tour de France—something the public could readily relate to—severely limited cycling's popular appeal. Some have suggested that the U.S., with its poor secondary roads and expansive distances, is simply not as bicycle-friendly as Europe. But I think there's no reason why cycling shouldn't enjoy the same degree of popularity here. Creating a greater public awareness about our rich cycling heritage is certainly a helpful step forward.

Matter: Critics were skeptical of the bicycle at many stages during its growth and metamorphosis: "When we reflect that the whole effort of this utilitarian age is to get away from labor and not into it, we can guess what the fate of the velocipede will ultimately be." Do you agree?

Herlihy: The bicycle has always been a bit of an anomaly from a technological perspective. For centuries, a few visionaries anticipated the peculiar advantages of a practical human-powered vehicle that would offer both healthy amusement and practical transportation. Yet the concept never quite fit the mold of conventional "progress," in that it employs rather than relieves physical labor. To truly appreciate the virtues of the bicycle, one must think about how much more efficiently it employs human power than the natural means of walking. It's really something of a mechanical miracle. As I recount in the book, until the basic bicycle came along in the 1860s, for decades, if not centuries, it was not even clear that human ingenuity could ever devise something that made better use of muscular powers for personal displacements. One must also think of the immense economical, ecological, and health benefits cycling offers over motorized means of transportation. The words of the *New York Times* correspondent who first came across a bicycle in Paris in 1867 still ring true today. "Is it not absurd, is it not a disgrace to the inventive age we live in, to see a man obliged to employ, in order to get through the street, a great vehicle, as large almost as a house? So let us have the velocipedes."

Matter: You write, "to feminists, the bicycle affirmed nothing less than the dignity and equality of women." How important and overlooked was the bicycle in promoting women's rights and possibly ushering in women's suffrage?

Herlihy: Certainly many who lived through the great boom of the 1890s concluded that the bicycle had exerted an enormous influence on the emerging "New Woman." I don't know if anyone has specifically examined how the cycling craze may have energized the suffrage movement, but a number of academic studies from the 1950s on have drawn a distinct connection between cycling at the turn-of-the-century and the budding women's liberation movement. To be sure, some revisionists have charged that the perceived relationship is overstated. My impression, however, is that the connection is very real and that the subject is still ripe for greater research.

Matter: How many bikes do you own and ride?

Herlihy: I'd say about ten, and I'd have even more if some of them hadn't been stolen over the years. Most are "vintage" Italian racers from the 1970s and 1980s. I no longer ride them all on a regular basis, but I still ride a Tommasini with Campy Super Record parts from time to time, even if I don't usually dress the part. I do most of my riding in and around Boston in regular clothes on a $300 city bike made in China. If books sales go well, however, I'd love to get something more contemporary and upscale; maybe a fancy mountain bike and/or a road racer made of some exotic material with all the latest components. Then I'll get fancy clip-less shoes and a Lycra outfit to go with it. But I'm likely to keep it fairly tame and heed the advice of one high-wheel rider who railed against those "vain and foolish men" who ride about in circus-like costumes flaunting "extraordinary combinations of colours."

Patrick Odenbeck

The Most Irrational

Here
.
"everything is arranged according to number"
precise
each falcon's path can be dictated in advance

all is golden
perfect in measure
2 for female, 3 for male, 5 for cohesion
6 for perfection, the pattern molded of clay
the things that are essential often go unnoticed
can you whisper to me in God's
language, numbers, zeros, decimal
points. Describe those great intentions to me in integers
2/3 or 3/2, initiate the design for the
perfect shape; "which the god used for embroidering the
constellations on the whole
heaven." After all it is common knowledge that
all that is beautiful
is difficult—the flawless alchemy within a shell's
hidden spiral.

Eleven is the sin
one more than the solid
ten is the old broken standard of stone
phrases; "the communion must be symmetric"
balance is always the most holy of places
numbers are gods

watch them interact in
ways we expect
or surprising us when they gravitate
on their own progressing the
fabric of life—moments answering slowly
in good faith
doing our taxes, balance checkbooks, calculate gas milage
worship
worship
locked in code or locked in thought
all modern prayer can be done on
a calculator

what elegant design

each person and equation, using equations, a number using
numbers
solving, dissolving, solving, solving, solving, solving, solving
taking away, adding to, dividing, breaking apart, adding, multiplying
multiplying, multiplying, multiplying, multiplying, multiplying, multiplying, together multiplying

differentiation—snowflake of six points
this in faces, in faces, in faces
points of five, pentagram points angles
for deciding
the core, the apple core, knowledge within the
palm; the hand, all intersections for
the future
decided
tools for manipulation
fingerprints and grasp on calculation
is five half the
story, secrets in reflection
in angles on the cusp of angel lips
where is the formula from and
can each

breathe without
calculation? Remember the subtle motion of infinity

there is a golden idea
out there
it can surface when least expected

all voices into one
there's harmony in the face of
a sunflower
watch it return to order, watch it terminate
depressed
each lamp head facing down leaves at side
all that holds them up is failing quite wonderfully.

the alcoholic,
the bourgeois, the
scientist, the quarterback, the
marksman, the con artist, the fish
eater, the deliverer, the soldier, the
radical, the makeshift, the country folk, the
airhead, the logistic, the player, the wannabe, the
clown, the courtier, the fake, the lesbian, the breast
reducer, the meter maid, the bondsman, the boater, the
loaf, the industrious, the legislator, the wicked, the lost,
the tribal, the queer eye, the hippy, the redundant, the
convincer, the elevator, the watcher, the seeker, the silent,
the scared, the weak, the evolutionary, the priest, the
therapist, the pusher, the addict, the forgetful, the soulless,
the fortunate, the senator, the delegate, the rapist, the baker,
the breast enlarger, the banker, the codependent, the
vegetarian, the cowgirl, the pharmacist, the transient, the
pissed off, the attorney, the reliever, the annoyed, the
attentive, the blind, the holistic, the contrived, the boys,
the cloud watcher, the hopeful, the enraged, the cook,
the christian, the fearful, the check bouncer, the
author, the conversationalist, the wonton, the
follower, the hated, the fucked, the divine, the
yolk, the friend, the rambler, the yodeler,
the veterinarian, the fisherman, the
ranger, the indian, the kabbalist,
the rationalist, the end.

Gary Norris

Introduction to Cultural Anthropology (limited stops)

Fifteen minutes late never early running behind sitting down. I am one among many wage earners. I like the ride; road houses yard by yard, crooked line of parked cars, fences chimneys trees, small shopping bags stuck whipping in the wind. I like noting day-to-day changes on each block. Got the trip down by turns. Yesterday at Conifer and Pine a rusting Corvair disappeared and with it the purple bunny on its dashboard. Its curbside space remains vacant—an oily rectangle containing two crushed Black Label cans and one dirty diaper. I had dreamt of driving it westward out of town on a three-lane expressway empty of cars, clouds of dust from past snow sandings and tarantellas on the AM radio, and now imagined it towed east through cracked streets circumferencing the lower downtown district, some sunken man in coveralls places it on a lift to be stripped. It would be crushed—one last tire popped outward, an elbow, an arc, half-makings of a once and always worn wheel dangles there in my thoughts, spun.

Last year I began carrying a small bag, and in it a legal pad, two pens, a paperback dictionary, eye drops, lip balm, and an old copy of *Robinson Crusoe*. I keep notes on the pad. I wet my eyes as they dry and keep my lips moist for comfort. I haven't read the book. I don't have time for it.

I really don't recommend using the bus to get around. If you must ride, pretend to be a cultural anthropologist. It doesn't take much to anthropologize; there's only a few simple ground rules. First, you must make lists. Second, you must recognize common patterns in random events. Third, you must draw your conclusions based on patterns not detail. Finally, should folks ever read your research, they are more likely to believe what you have written if they can easily relate it to their own experiences.

One day I was too tired to get out of bed. My cat really didn't want to move anyway. I was on my back, hands clasped on my chest. I stared at the ceiling. The fan circled too quickly to see the five white blades distinctly, though I still see the black line dancing silently within its own ellipses in the radius of the greater blur—a result of the broom handle getting stuck into the moving fan while I bent to look under the bed months ago. I looked at the ceiling, tried very hard to empty my head, took short breaths through my nose. All I wanted to see and think was ceiling—flat white cool plaster close to concrete not moving not distant, always out of reach. At four twenty-five I stretched my arms up to pull it all down in a series of strong dramatic grasps. Unsuccessful, I took a shower and went back to bed.

The sky was empty the next morning. Not a cloud in sight. No cars sped by leaving vapor and sand. No birds. I stood hands against my pant legs, erect and ahead. I noticed the telephone pole across the street is anchored at a slight angle. The street sidewalk yards and homes seemed to have torqued it—the whole block uses it as a crutch. I wondered when it will break, flinging my neighbors' homes hurly burly into the horizon. The bus startled me as the driver stopped, door precisely at my feet.

Silence burst in two hydraulic gasps. I walked to the back seats affected. I heard the word love, smelled aftershave perspiration urine peppermint booze. My vision blurred. My hands shook. My heart broke. I remembered Carlene, a black girl from summer camp who wandered the grounds and lake after lights out with me talking politics—eyes, two darts flung from the dark trees and purple water at me. *Your folks are bigots*, she said and kissed me. That fall she sent me a picture—her in a cheerleader's outfit—and a short letter that explained her desire for us to move in together outside of Muskogee. We both had a fondness for the Arkansas River, flash floods, and hailstorms. I never wrote back.

When I leave the bus I walk to the library and browse the shelves like I always do. I look for something to catch my eye rather than wait; I drag my fingers across books' spines, thwack my way row after row. Once I found a book written by a cultural anthropologist from some New York university about how people talked about their jobs. It was mostly interviews mixed with detailed descriptions about folks' behavior at work and home. Each chapter was named after a subject and ended with the author's conclusions.

The anthropologist arrives at her conclusions by comparing her descriptions with her subjects' statements.

One memorable story is about a guy called Tim to protect his anonymity. Tim drinks malt liquor and wears the same pants. He struggles to make cell phone payments and spends hot summer days at the OTB with his pals Smarty and Pete. In the book Tim yells at his girl Cheri and swats flies. He relates tales of a misspent youth that he is still living and truancy; he speaks about the economy. Eventually Tim takes a job at McDonald's. He complains about lack of fulfillment and funds. The anthropologist concludes that Tim is depressed. *Because of our consumer culture, he cannot afford his appetite for living*. She finds him attractive yet repulsive.

The next day I boarded the bus with pad and pencil.

I often get carried away while taking notes. I gasp or laugh. I have cried on occasion. I read about how to conduct field research and have tried to become invisible.

One day I showed up in brown. I ironed my old coveralls the night before. I bought a Browns baseball cap. I thought I would blend in with some color. I thought I would go unnoticed. Unfortunately, the riders stared at me. So, now I dress like I always did, like a guy like me always does. And when I write I chew on my pen cap, suck on the collecting spit, make educated moans, and beam with delight.

I create names for the different kinds of people I observe. Some of my recent notes include the following categories: The Ritually Unclean, Obese Riders, Public Masturbators, Baby Sensationalists, Driver Talkers, Linguists, Fashion Fans, Foot-tappers, Bible Readers, Lady-lookers, and Spontaneous Conversationalists. I have had to chronologically organize my notes within files grouped according to category. A typical day provides substantial opportunity for revision.

For example: I board, show ID, and sit in the middle of things. I always make a show of taking out my tools. I slowly open my bag. The Velcro fasteners rip loudly apart. The tearing noise claws at the air and quiets things for a moment. The riders look at me (I do this everyday) and I look at them. This sets a mood. I look around, smile and open my notebook. I shake my head in affirmation to show them I am working. I take notes.

Baby Sensationalist.
BS holds daughter too high above left shoulder aisle-side hoping people will recognize her holding baby too high skylarks for attention baby cries because she is shaken too hard and doesn't like her little tummy forced up and down against mother's shoulder too high.
BS lets her baby down upon her thighs and talks to her in baby talk how's my little fatty puss snuggle honey and baby still cries embarrassed probably and passengers smile in an effort to make BS stop but she won't because she does it every morning for twenty minutes from Conifer to downtown.

You have to keep notes quick and sort it all out later because the most important thing for a cultural anthropologist is to respect the performance. You must recognize the performer and offer encouragement with inviting gestures. I wink at the mother when she looks behind her. She giggles at her fellow riders because of her baby's fuss. I wink at her, slightly nod, and smile warmly; I acknowledge her effort. I learned this from the girl behind the counter at Skaggs.

Before I write, I tap my pad three times and clear my throat.
"Yes." Quietly, meaningfully, professionally. It is my only word on the bus.
"Yes." The rest is sounds. Hmmmm tap tap tap "Yes," chew on the cap, write.
The bus groans shakes pops breathes and drives. I lean my head on the window glass and rest my eyes. The bus massages my scalp, rubs my brain, and quiets my mind. As my solid

thoughts begin to loosen, I begin to drift and daydream. I often dream of buses.

I have many recurring dreams. In "My Mother the Vampire," I am out killing bloodsuckers with my friend Alex. We were eight when I first had this dream but now we're much older, except that Alex still looks about ten. We kill vampires with lilies. Larger than actual lilies, these petals rise and curve long and white with blackish not green veins. They are sticky and pregnant with yellow pollen. Getting a vampire to take a flower that will ultimately kill it isn't as easy as it sounds. Vampires are suspicious of gifts.

I always return to my childhood home at the end of the day and find my mother in her floral nightgown on our old couch. She lies quite peacefully on its green cushions like she is taking a nap. Her even breaths are soothing. I can hear my brothers in the bedroom down the hall. There is a turntable in the room. A scratchy copy of The Beach Boys "Wouldn't it be Nice?" is playing. A-side, Capitol Records, the side I scratched good, messing with what didn't belong to me. She slowly sits up and asks for a hug. I wake up.

There are other dreams like "Rest Stop Stall" and "All My Teeth are Falling Out." I keep notes about dreams, too. My most recent recurring dream is "The Quiet Bus." I get on a silver bus, like one of those mobile homes but more rectangular, and sit in the back. There is no sound. The bus glides around sharp corners and slides across treacherous potholes. There are large windows on the sides and in back to provide wonderful views. It never takes a red light and always accelerates. The driver wears thick workman's gloves and furiously turns the steering wheel with both hands—hand over hand over hand—to keep us on course. As my body gives up to increasing speeds, I try to warn the five or six other passengers about possible dangers. My voice is so quiet. Whisper whisper whisper like scratching and thin, crumpling paper as we take on a hill. At its crest the bus leaves the ground. Silently floating across a city park, the driver announces a number of destinations: Bathroom, Toilet, Faucet, Paper, Whicker Hamper, Floor.

The bus turns and we move down into the city. It is one big hill the rest of the way. We leave the homes behind. We leave the grass and gardens, bushes and trees. Riders become quiet as the sun illuminates and warms us. Individuals give way to the crowd. Hang up cell phones. Finish small talk. Close bags. Clench purses. Straighten ties. Put feet on the floor. Anticipate the day. On warm mornings the wheels mimic the riders and zip open and shut the tar-sealed cracks on the asphalt avenues. In the winter, these are silent circles.

I saw a dark spot on my ceiling turned out to be a spider that laid eggs under my bed whose babies chewed at my skin, gathering it together into dozens of red smarting sores. Little bits of information. Red-dotted notes. Black rotting spider. White plaster ceiling. A bus transfer in a half-wad on my dresser with almost visible date and times, numbers losing order. My cat, stoic, endures.

Bin Ramke

Animal Intelligence

We think they are serene, as in what we think we want
from weather: serene derived from dry, sere —
a dry mind amid mountains. A kind of minding.

Ghost is a guess of anatomy, a moderation of flesh —
the wet flesh renounced, repulsed — and a lover
returning home during seasonal darkness

creeps warily, wound up, wounding flesh,
this battered better self become, becoming hard;
hard to say why he so loved sadness, the equivalent

of evening, only the glancing light which goes
by many names crepuscular but not enough to read by,
only to linger. This is so maddening about dreams,

the sanity all called to the waking side, the sleep
a sacrament, a sly response or inebriate virtue,
a tantalus of call and response. Wound this way,

a tightened tangent of anguish, a dream
ascends into consciousness: some claim to
remember, others make it up as they recall,

watching your eyes for signs.
Oh, and some claimed to dream in grisaille, (black
and white vision invented by photography (about

the time dreams became symptoms)) black
and white the boundaries—I would draw my
dreams with crayon, pencil, charcoal,

for instance, the one about the lover returning
home into the mountains one dry evening.
For instance, a lead animal will stop to look at a moving chain

and move his head back and forth in rhythm with its swing.
He isn't concerned about being slaughtered: he's afraid
of a small piece of chain that jiggles and looks out of place.
        --Temple Grandin, *Thinking in Pictures*

The woman (I loved) explained to me
that I wanted the praise only of strangers—
my own crowd never enough. Good enough. No,

she said, You never ask for fear of getting.
She faded ferocious. Wounded.
It wound about itself: caduceus (a symbol

of course but also a snake. A pair of snakes.
DNA-like twined night and day and delirious
with it within it.) A sound, another pianoish

dripping—(paired parentheses like snakes?)
wintry, sun a glitter of ices—or summer,
an agon of music like anger, water,

singular a nobility, of patience.
Another ghost is a kindness.
Recognition of one's kind

the wise call generosity. It is
to join of your own group...
ghastly, a pale demarcation of season, ending.

"As a child I fell ill of hunger and fear"
said a child who felt anger and cheered
himself with a gang of toys, a group—

Whose child is full of fear? Weather
like distance, like choice—
some word for winter. Conscious, the word,

derives—from rivus, stream, and from
from—from words for knowing and
for cut.

        To segment the sky, the ocean,
the vast plain of mind, human, latitude
and longitude, x and y, street and avenue—

thus the goose crosses some grid
into some other grid, unaware of himself as
I would make him, glorious and serene.

Dry smoke drifts and turbulence cleanses
the memory (the fair emergency of trauma
the emerged mother,) smoke drifts turbulent

if gentle, winding clearly among the fictions
arising from the smolder the wreckage,
rising little soldiers, factions among the fortunes.

What Goes Up...
Derrick Jensen

As a long-time grassroots environmental activist, and as a creature living in the thrashing endgame of civilization, I am intimately acquainted with the landscape of loss, and have grown accustomed to carrying the daily weight of despair. I have walked clear-cuts that wrap around mountains, drop into valleys, then climb ridges to fragment watershed after watershed, and I've sat silent near empty streams that two generations ago were "lashed into whiteness" by innumerable salmon coming home to spawn and die.

A few years ago I began to feel pretty apocalyptic. But I hesitated to use that word, in part because of those drawings I've seen of crazy penitents carrying "The End is Near" signs, and in part because of the power of the word itself. Apocalypse. I didn't want to use it lightly.

But then a friend and fellow activist said, "What will it take for you to finally call it an apocalypse? The death of the salmon? Global warming? The ozone hole? The reduction of krill populations off Antarctica by ninety percent, the turning of the sea off San Diego into a dead zone, the same for the Gulf of Mexico? How about the end of the great coral reefs? The extirpation of two hundred species per day? Four hundred? Six hundred? Give me a specific threshold, Derrick, a specific point at which you will finally use that word."

Thanks, George.

Do you believe that our culture will undergo a voluntary transformation to a sane and sustainable way of living?

I didn't think you would. I don't either, and neither does anyone I talk to. For the last couple of years I've taken to asking people this question, at talks and rallies, in libraries, on buses, in airplanes, at the grocery store, the hardware store. Everywhere. The answers range from emphatic *no*'s to laughter. No one answers in the affirmative. One fellow at one talk did raise his hand, and when everyone looked at him, he dropped his hand, then said, sheepishly, "Oh, voluntary? Of course not." My next question: how would this understanding—that our culture will not voluntarily stop destroying the natural world, eliminating indigenous cultures, exploiting the poor, and killing those who resist—shift our strategy or tactics? The answer? Nobody knows, because we never talk about it.

I just got home from talking to a new friend, another long-time activist. She told me of a campaign in which she participated in a few years ago to try to stop the government and transnational timber corporations from spraying agent orange, a potent defoliant and teratogen, in the forests of Oregon. Whenever activists learned that a hillside was going to be sprayed, they assembled there, hoping their presence would stop the poisoning. But each time, like clockwork, the helicopters appeared, and each time, like clockwork, the helicopters dumped their loads of Agent Orange onto the hillside, onto the protesting activists. The campaign did not succeed.

"But," she said to me, "I'll tell you

what did. A bunch of Vietnam vets lived back in those hills, and they sent messages to the Bureau of Land Management, and to Weyerhaeuser, Boise Cascade, and the other timber companies, saying, 'We know the names of your helicopter pilots, and we know their addresses.'"

I waited for her to finish.

"You know what happened next?" she asked.

"I think I do," I responded.

"Exactly," she said. "The spraying stopped."

On Tuesday, 11 September 2001, the twin towers of the World Trade Center collapsed, killing thousands of people. That same day one portion of the Pentagon also collapsed, killing more than one hundred. In addition, a jet airliner crashed in Pennsylvania.

Let's tell this story again: On Tuesday, 11 September 2001, nineteen Arab terrorists unleashed their fanaticism on the United States by hijacking four planes, each containing scores of innocent victims. These terrorists, who do not value life the way we Americans do, slammed two of these planes into the World Trade Center, and a third into the Pentagon. Courageous men and women in the fourth plane wrestled with their attackers and drove the plane into the ground, sacrificing themselves rather than allowing the killers to attack the headquarters of the CIA, or any other crucial targets. Our government is still trying to find and punish those who masterminded the attack. This will be difficult because, as our President, George W Bush, said, "This enemy hides in shadows and has no regard for human life. This is an enemy that [sic] preys on innocent and unsuspecting people and then runs for cover."[1] When we find them, we must kill them. This killing will not be easy on us. We must steel ourselves against the possibility—inevitability—that we may be forced to kill even those whose guilt we cannot finally establish. As former Secretary of State Lawrence Eagleburger said, "There is only one way to begin to deal with people like this, and that is you have to kill some of them even if they are not immediately directly involved in this thing."[2] Many politicians and journalists have spoken yet more directly. "This is no time," syndicated columnist (and bestselling author) Ann Coulter wrote, "to be precious about locating the exact individuals directly involved in this particular terrorist attack…We should invade their countries, kill their leaders and convert them to Christianity."[3]

Here is another version of the same story: On Tuesday, 11 September 2001, nineteen young men made their mothers proud. They gave their lives in order to strike a blow against the United States, the greatest terrorist state ever to exist. This blow was struck in response to US support for the dispossession and murder of Palestinians, to the forced installation of pro-Western governments in Saudi Arabia, Egypt, and many other countries, to the hundreds of thousands of Iraqi civilians killed by US bombs, and to the irradiation of

Iraq with depleted uranium. More broadly, it was a response to the CIA-backed murder in Indonesia of 650,000 human beings, and to the hundreds of thousands murdered by US-backed death squads in Central and South America. To the four million civilians killed in North Korea. To the nine thousand babies who die every month as a direct result of US sanctions on Iraq. To the theft of American Indian land and the killings of millions of Indians. To the overthrow of democratically-elected governments around the world and the imposition of business-friendly dictators like Idi Amin, the Shah, or Ferdinand Marcos. (As Secretary of Defense, William Cohen said to a group of *Fortune* 500 leaders, "Business follows the flag. . . We provide the security. You provide the investment."[4] Even here, however, Cohen was being disingenuous, since because of corporate welfare programs "we" generally provide the investment as well.) To an American foreign policy driven by the needs of industrial production—as manifested through the unnatural logic of the bottom line—not life. This was a blow delivered not only against the United States but against a murderous global economy—a half million babies die each year as a direct result of so-called debt repayment[5]—that is a continuation of the same old colonialism under which those who exploit get rich, and the rest get killed. The poor of the world would all be better off if the global economy—run by transnational corporations backed by the military power of the United States—disappeared tomorrow. When a country, an economy, and a culture are all based on the systematic violent exploitation of humans and nonhumans the world over, it should come as no surprise when at long last someone fights back. We can only hope and pray that the organizations behind this have the resources and stamina to keep at it until they bring down the global economy.

Here's another version: Tuesday, 11 September 2001, was a tragedy for the planet, and at least a temporary victory for rage and hatred. But let us not seek to pinpoint blame, nor meet negativity with negativity. The terrorists were wrong to act as they did, but to meet their violence with our own would be just as wrong. Violence never solves anything. As Gandhi said, "An eye for an eye only ends up making the whole world blind." Another way to put this is that even if you believe that the United States and the global economy are fundamentally destructive, you cannot use the master's tools to dismantle the master's house. This means the most important thing any of us can do is eradicate the anger that lies within our own hearts, and that wounds the world as surely as do all the hijackers in Afghanistan, and all the bombs in the United States. If I wish to experience peace, I must provide peace for another. If I wish to heal my own anger, I must heal the anger of another. I know that all the terrorists of the world are, beneath it all, searching for love. It is the task of those of us who've been granted this understanding to teach them this, simply by loving them, and then by loving them more. For love is the only cure. I deplore violence, and if the United States goes to war, I will oppose that war in whatever peaceful ways I can, with love in my heart. And I will love and support our brave troops.

Or how about this: It should be clear to everyone by now—even those with a vested interest in ignorance—that industrial civilization is killing the planet. It is causing unprecedented human privation and suffering. Unless it is stopped, or somehow stops itself, or most likely collapses under the weight of its inherent ecological and human destructiveness, it will kill every living being on earth. It should be equally clear that to this point, the efforts of those of us working to stop or slow the destruction are insufficient to the task. We file our lawsuits, write our books, send letters to editors, representatives, CEOs, carry signs and placards, restore natural communities, and not only do we not stop or slow the destruction, but it actually continues to accelerate. Rates of deforestation continue to rise, rates of extinction do the same, global warming proceeds apace, the rich get richer, the poor starve to death, and the world burns.

At the same time we find ourselves so-often-seemingly-helplessly facing down civilization's speeding train of destruction, we find also there is a huge gap in our discourse. We speak much of the tactics of civil disobedience, much of the spiritual politics of cultural transformation, much of the sciences of biotechnology, toxicology, biology, and psychology. We talk of law. We also talk often of despair, frustration, and sorrow. There is

not one of us who has not personally and directly experienced great loss.

Yet our discourse remains firmly embedded in that which is sanctioned by the very overarching structure that governs the destruction in the first place. We do not often speak of the tactics of sabotage, and even less do we speak of violence. We avoid them, or pretend they should not be allowed to enter even the realm of possibility, or that they simply do not exist, like disinherited relatives who show up at a family reunion.

A few years ago I interviewed a long-term and well-respected Gandhian activist. I asked him, "What if those in power are murderous? What if they're not willing to listen to reason at all? Should we continue to approach them nonviolently?"

He responded, reasonably enough, "When a house is on fire, and has gone far beyond the point where you can do anything about it, all you can do is bring lots of water to try to stop its spread. But you can't save the house. Nonviolence is a precautionary principle. Before the house is on fire you have to make sure you have a fire hydrant, clearly marked escape routes, emergency exits. The same is true in society. You educate your children in nonviolence. You educate your media in nonviolence. And when someone has a grievance, you don't ignore or suppress it, but you listen to that person, and ask, 'What is your concern?' You say, 'Let's sit down and solve it.'"

I agreed with what he said, so far as it went, but that agreement didn't stop me from understanding that he'd sidestepped the question.

Before I could bring him back, he continued. "Say a father beats his children. Once he has already reached that stage, you have to say, 'What kind of a childhood did he have? How did he not learn the skills of coping with adverse situations in a calm, compassionate, composed way?'"

This Gandhian's compassion, I thought, was entirely misplaced. Where was his compassion for the children being beaten? What few discussions we as a movement have concerning the question of violence seem always to follow this pattern, of quickly demanding compassion for the perpetrators while conveniently forgetting the victims, and more to the point, not stopping the original abuse. I responded that I believed the first question we need to ask is how we can get the children to a safe place. Once safety has been established, by any means possible, I said, and once the emotional needs of the children are being met, only then do we have the luxury of asking about the father's emotional needs, and his history.

What happened next is really the point of this story. I asked this devoted adherent of nonviolence if in his mind it would ever be acceptable to commit an act of violence were it determined to be the only way to save the children. His answer was revealing, and symbolizes the hole in our discourse: he changed the subject.

After I transcribed and edited the interview, I sent it to him with a new question inserted, attempting once again to pin him down. What did he do this time? He deleted my question.

Too often this is the response of all of us when faced with this most difficult of questions: when is violence an appropriate response in attempting to stop injustice? But with the world dying—or rather being killed—we no longer have the luxury to change the subject or to delete the question. The question will not go away.

I had two reasons for telling the four versions of the World Trade Center bombing. The first was simply to point out that all writers are propagandists. Writers who claim differently, or who otherwise do not understand this, have succumbed to the extremely dangerous propaganda that narrative can be divorced from value. This is not true. All descriptions carry with them weighty presumptions of value. This is as true for wordless descriptions such as mathematical formulae—which value the quantifiable and ignore everything else—as it is for the descriptions I gave above. The first version, by giving only current actions—"the twin towers of the World Trade Center collapsed, killing thousands of people"— devalues (by their absence) cause and context. Why did the towers collapse? What were the events surrounding the collapse? This neat excision of both cause and context is the standard in capitalist journalism (I used to call it mainstream journalism, then discovered the more accurate corporate journalism, and recently have simply taken to calling it what it is, as the capitalist media are written, edited, produced, and most importantly owned by capitalists, top to bottom), where, for example, we often hear of devastating mudslides in the colonies killing thousands of people who were foolish enough to build villages beneath unstable slopes. Toward the end of these articles we sometimes see sidelong references to "illegal logging," but nowhere do we see mention of Weyerhaeuser, Hyundai, Daishowa, or other transnational timber companies which cut the steep slopes over the objections—and sometimes dead bodies—of the villagers. Or we may read of the rebel group UNITA slaughtering civilians in Angola, with no mention of two decades of US financial and moral support for this group. So far as the bombing of the World Trade Center, despite yard after column yard devoted to the attacks, analyses of potential reasons for hatred of the United States rarely venture beyond, "They're fanatics," or "They're jealous of our lifestyle," or even, and I'm not making this up, "They want our resources."

The second, patriotic version carries with it the inherent presumption that the United States did nothing to deserve the attack. If the United States kills citizens of other countries, and survivors of that violence respond by killing United States citizens— even if the casualty counts of the counter-strikes are by any realistic assessment much smaller—the United States is then justified in killing yet more citizens of those other countries. This forms, of course, a powerful historical continuity to the conquest of North America, as white massacres of Indians are too numerous to count, much less commemorate, yet Indian (counter) attacks on whites were avenged many orders of magnitude over: as Thomas Jefferson put it, "In war, they will kill some of us; we shall destroy all of them."[6] Another presumption of the patriotic version is that the lives of people killed by foreign terrorists are more worthy of notice, vengeance, and future protection than those killed, for example, by unsafe working conditions, or by the turning of our total environment into a carcinogenic stew. Close to three thousand people died in those attacks. In no way do I mean to demean these lives once presumably full of love, friendship, drama, sorrow, and so on—these three thousand stories cut short—but more Americans die each month from toxins and other workplace hazards, and more Americans die each *week* from *preventable* cancers, that is carcinogens and other hazards that are for the most part direct results of the activities of large corporations, and certainly the results of the industrial economy.[7] The lack of outrage over these deaths commensurate to the outrage expressed over the deaths in the bombing of the World Trade Center reveals much—if we care to reflect on it—about the values and presumptions of our culture.

The third version, from the perspective of the bombers or their supporters, presumes that there are conditions under which it is morally acceptable to kill noncombatants, to kill those who themselves have done you no direct harm.[8] It also presumes that to kill people within the United States (by bombs, of course, since carcinogens spewed in the service of production evidently do not count as causes of atrocity) may cause those who run the governments of the United States—both nominal, that is, political, and de facto, that is, economic—to re-think their position of violently dominating the rest of the planet.

The fourth version presumes it is possible to halt or significantly slow violence through nonviolent means.

Closely allied to all of this is my second reason, which is that the same action can often seem immoral from one perspective and moral from another. What's more, the same action can often *be* moral from one perspective and immoral from another. From the perspective, for example, of salmon or other creatures, including humans, whose lives depend on free-flowing rivers, dams are murderous and immoral. To remove dams would from this perspective be extremely moral. Those who make money from the generation of hydroelectricity, or who irrigate from reservoirs, or who live downriver and who very well might be killed if the dams were suddenly to burst, would probably take a dim view of the morality of someone intentionally blowing up the Grand Coulee or Glen Canyon dams. Of course the most moral thing to have done—defining *morality* in this case as an action that promotes life—would have been to not build these or any other large dams in the first place. But they're built, and they continue to be built the world over,

to the consistent short-term fiscal benefit of huge corporations—really the primary consideration of any political decision—and over the determined yet usually unsuccessful resistance of the poor. The second most moral thing to do—continuing to use the aforementioned definition—would be to let the water out slowly, and then breach the dams more or less gently, taking the survival needs (as opposed to the more abstract requirements of our economic system) of all humans and nonhumans into account as we let rivers once again run free. But the dams are there, and they're killing the rivers—so far as dams in the Northwest, salmon and sturgeon are fast disappearing from the region, and so far as Glen Canyon, I'm not sure what more I need to say except that the Colorado River no longer even reaches the ocean—and the current political, economic, and social systems have shown themselves to not only be consistently unresponsive but irredeemably detrimental to human and nonhuman needs. Faced with a choice between healthy functioning natural communities on one hand and profits on the other (or beneath those profits, and motivating them, the centralization of power) of course those in power always choose the latter. What, then, becomes the most moral thing to do? Do we stand by and watch the last of the salmon die? Do we write letters and file lawsuits that we know in our hearts will ultimately not make much difference, or do we take out the dams ourselves?

Here are more questions: what would the rivers themselves want? Would it cause them additional pain to have the dams blown, or would they perceive that as their release from a cement cage?

I am aiming at a far more profound target than the nearly twelve million cubic yards of cement that went into the Grand Coulee Dam. I want to examine the morality and feasability of intentionally taking down not just dams but all of civilization. I aim to examine this as unflinchingly and honestly as I can, even, or especially, at the risk of examining topics normally considered off-limits to discourse.

I am not the first to make the case that the industrial economy, indeed, civilization (which underpins and gives inevitable rise to it), is incompatible with human and nonhuman freedoms, and in fact with human and nonhuman life.[9] If you accept that the industrial economy—and beneath it, civilization—is destroying the planet and creating unprecedented human suffering among the poor (and if you don't accept this, go ahead and put this book down, back away slowly, turn on the television, and take some more *soma*; the drug should kick in soon enough, your agitation will disappear, you'll forget everything I've said, and then everything will be perfect again, just like the voices from the television tell you over and over), then it becomes clear that the best thing that can happen, from the perspective of essentially all nonhumans as well as the vast majority of humans, is for the industrial economy (and civilization) to go away, or in the shorter run for it to be slowed as much as humanly possible during the time we await its final collapse. But here's the problem: this slowing of the industrial economy will inconvenience many of those who benefit from it, including nearly everyone in the United States. Many of those who will be inconvenienced identify so much more with their role as participants in the industrial economy than they do with being human that they may very well consider this inconvenience to be a threat to their very lives. The salient point is that those people will not allow themselves to be inconvenienced without a fight. What, then, becomes the right thing to do? Here's another way to ask this: is it possible to talk about fundamental social change without asking ourselves the question the Gandhian refused to answer, and many other questions as well?

If I'm going to contemplate (and if appropriate, help bring about) the collapse of civilization, I need to define what it is I may very well want to bring down. *Webster's* calls civilization "a high stage of social and cultural development." The *Oxford English Dictionary* describes it as "a developed or advanced state of human society." All the other dictionaries I checked were similarly laudatory. These definitions, no matter how broadly shared, helped me not in the slightest. They seemed to me hopelessly sloppy. After reading them, I still had no idea what the hell a civilization is; define *high*, *developed*, or *advanced*, please. The definitions, it struck me, are also extremely self-serving; can you imagine writers of dictionaries willingly classifying themselves as members of "a low, undeveloped, or backward state of human society"?

I suddenly remembered that all writers, including writers of dictionaries, are propagandists, and realized that these definitions are, in fact, bite-sized chunks of propaganda, concise articulations of the arrogance that has led those who believe they are living in the most advanced—and best— culture to attempt to impose by force this way of being on all others.

I would define a civilization much more precisely, and I believe more usefully, as a culture—that is, a complex of stories, institutions, and artifacts—that both leads to and emerges from the growth of cities (*civilization*, see *civil*: from *civis*, meaning *citizen*, from latin *civitatis*, meaning *state* or *city*), with cities being defined, so as to distinguish them from camps, villages, and so on, as people living more or less permanently in one place in densities high enough to require the routine importation of food and other necessities of life. Thus a Tolowa village five hundred years ago where I live in Tu'nes (*meadow long* in the Tolowa tongue), now called Crescent City, California, would not have been a city, since the Tolowa ate native salmon, clams, deer, huckleberries, and so on, and had no need to bring in food from outside. Thus, under my definition, the Tolowa, because their way of living was not characterized by the growth of cities, would not have been civilized. On the other hand, the Aztecs were. Their social structure led inevitably to great cities like Iztapalapa and Tenochtitlán, the latter of which was, when Europeans first encountered it, far larger than any city in Europe, with a population five times that of London or Seville.[10] Shortly before razing Tenochtitlán and slaughtering or enslaving its inhabitants, the explorer and conquistador Hernando Cortés remarked that it was easily the most beautiful city on earth.[11] Beautiful or not, Tenochtitlán required, as do all cities, the (often forced) importation of food and other resources. The story of any civilization is the story of the rise of cities, which means it is the story of the funneling of resources toward these cities (in order to sustain them and cause them to grow), which means it is the story of an increasing region of unsustainability surrounded by an increasingly exploited countryside.

But there's more. Cities do not arise in political, social, and ecological vacuums. Lewis Mumford, in the second book of his two-volume *Myth of the Machine*, uses the term *civilization* "to denote the group of institutions that first took form under kingship. Its chief features, constant in varying proportions throughout history, are the centralization of political power, the separation of classes, the lifetime division of labor, the mechanization of production, the magnification of military power, the economic exploitation of the weak, and the universal introduction of slavery and forced labor for both industrial and military purposes."[12] (The anthropologist and philosopher Stanley Diamond put this a bit more succinctly when he noted, "Civilization originates in conquest abroad and repression at home."[13]) These attributes, which inhere not just in our culture but in all civilizations, make civilization sound pretty bad. But, according to Mumford, civilization has another, more benign face as well. He continues, "These institutions would have completely discredited both the primal myth of divine kingship and the derivative myth of the machine had they not been accompanied by another set of collective traits that deservedly claim admiration: the invention and keeping of the written record, the growth of visual and musical arts, the effort to widen the circle of communication and economic intercourse far beyond the range of any local community: ultimately the purpose to make available to all men [sic] the discoveries and inventions and creations, the works of art and thought, the values and purposes that any single group has discovered."[14]

Much as I admire and have been influenced by Mumford's work, I fear that when he began discussing civilization's admirable face he fell under the spell to the same propaganda promulgated by the lexicographers whose work I consulted; that our culture really is "advanced," or "higher." But if we dig beneath this second, smiling mask of civilization—the perception that civilization's visual or musical arts, for example, are more developed than those of non-civilized peoples—we find a mirror image of civilization's other face; that of power. It wouldn't be entirely accurate to say that visual and musical arts have particularly *grown* under our system; it would be more

accurate to say they have long ago succumbed to the same division of labor that characterizes our economics, politics, and in fact the rest of art. Instead of visual or musical arts being primarily participatory—important parts of the dailiness of the lives of everyone, as I have experienced among the traditional indigenous people I have known, the uncivilized, where songs are sung by everyone as means to bond members of the community to each other and to their land base—within civilization, songs are written and performed more often by experts, those with "talent," those whose lives are devoted to the production of these arts. There's no reason for me to listen to my neighbor sing (probably off-key) some amateurish song of his own invention when I can pop in a CD of Beethoven, Mozart, or Lou Reed (okay, so Lou Reed sings off-key, too, but I like it). I'm not certain I would characterize the conversion of human beings from participants in the ongoing creation of communal arts to more passive consumers of artistic products manufactured by distant experts—even if these distant experts are *really* talented—as a good thing.

I could make a similar argument about writing, but Stanley Diamond beat me to it: "Writing was one of the original mysteries of civilization, and it reduced the complexities of experience to the written word. Moreover, writing provides the ruling classes with an ideological instrument of incalculable power. The word of God becomes an invincible law, mediated by priests; therefore, respond the Iroquois, confronting the European: 'Scripture was written by the Devil.' With the advent of writing, symbols became explicit; they lost a certain richness. Man's [sic] word was no longer an endless exploration of reality, but a sign that could be used against him. . . for writing splits consciousness in two ways — it becomes more authoritative than talking, thus degrading the meaning of speech and eroding oral tradition; and it makes it possible to use words for the political manipulation and control of others. Written signs supplant memory; an official, fixed and permanent version of events can be made. If it is written, in early civilizations [and I would suggest, now], it is bound to be true."[15]

I have two problems, also, with Mumford's claim that the widening of communication and economic intercourse under civilization benefits people as a whole. The first is that it presumes that uncivilized people do not communicate or participate in economic transactions beyond their local communities. Many do. Shells from the Northwest Coast found their way into the hands of Plains Indians, and buffalo robes often ended up on the coast. (And let's not *even* talk about non-civilized people communicating with their nonhuman neighbors, something rarely practiced by the civilized — talk about restricting yourself to your own community!) In any case, I'm not certain that the ability to send emails back and forth to Spain or to watch television programs beamed out of Los Angeles makes my life particularly richer. It's far more important, useful, and enriching, I think, to get to know my neighbors. I'm frequently amazed to find myself sitting in a room full of fellow human beings, all of us staring at a box watching and listening to a story enacted by people far away. I have friends who know Seinfeld's neighbors better than their own. I, too, can get lost in valuing the unreality of the distant over that which surrounds me every day. I have to confess I can navigate the mazes of the computer game *Doom2: Hell on Earth* far better than I can find my way along the labyrinthine game trails beneath the trees outside my window, and I understand the intricacies of Word for Windows far better than I do the complex dance of rain, sun, predators, prey, scavengers, plants, and soil in the creek one hundred yards away. The other night, I wrote till late, and finally turned off my computer to step outside and say goodnight to the dogs. I realized, then, that the wind was blowing hard through the tops of the redwood trees, and the trees were sighing and whispering. Branches were clashing, and in the distance I heard them cracking. Until that moment I had not realized such a symphony was taking place so near, much less had I gone out to participate in it, to feel the wind blow my hair and to feel the tossed rain hit me in the face. All of the sounds of the night had been drowned out by the monotone whine of my computer's fan. Just yesterday I saw a couple of hooded mergansers playing on the pond outside my bedroom. Then last night I saw a television program in which yet another lion chased yet another zebra. Which of those two scenes makes me richer? This perceived widening of communication is just another replication of the problem of the visual and musical arts, because given the impulse for centralized control that motivates civilization, widening communication in this case really means reducing us from active participants in our own lives and in the lives of those around us to consumers sucking words and images from some distant sugar tit.

I have another problem with Mumford's statement. In claiming that the widening of communication and economic intercourse are admirable, he seems to have forgotten—and this is strange, considering the normal sophistication of his analysis— that this widening can only be universally beneficial when all parties act voluntarily and under circumstances of relatively equivalent power. I'd hate to have to make the case, for example, that the people of Africa—perhaps 100 million of whom died because of the slave trade, and many more of whom find themselves dispossessed and/or impoverished today—have benefited from their "economic intercourse" with Europeans. The same can be said for Aborigines, Indians, the people of pre-contact India, and so on.

I want to re-examine one other thing Mumford wrote, in part because he makes an argument for civilization I've seen replicated so many times elsewhere, and that actually leads, I think, to some of the very serious problems we face today. He concluded the section I quoted above, and I reproduce it here just so you don't have to flip back a couple of pages: "ultimately the purpose [is] to make available to all men [sic] the discoveries and inventions and creations, the works of art and thought, the values and purposes that any single group has discovered." But just as a widening of economic intercourse is only beneficial to everyone when all exchanges are voluntary, so, too, the imposition of one group's values and purposes onto another, or its appropriation of the other's discoveries, can lead only to the exploitation and diminution of the latter in favor of the former. That this "exchange" helps all was commonly argued by early Europeans in America, as when Captain John Chester wrote that the Indians were to gain "the knowledge of our faith," while the Europeans would harvest "such ritches as the country hath."[16] It was argued as well by American slave owners in the nineteenth century. Philosopher George Fitzhugh stated that "slavery educates, refines, and moralizes the masses by bringing them into continual intercourse with masters of superior minds, information, and morality."[17] And it's just as commonly argued today by those who would teach the virtues of blue jeans, Big Macs™, Coca-Cola™, Capitalism™, and Jesus Christ™ to the world's poor in exchange for dispossessing them of their land base and forcing them to work in sweatshops.

Another problem is that Mumford's statement reinforces a mindset that leads inevitably to unsustainability, because it presumes that discoveries, inventions, creations, works of art and thought, and values and purposes are transposable over space; that is, that they are separable from both the human context and land base that created them. Mumford's statement unintentionally reveals perhaps more than anything else the power of the stories that hold us in thralldom to the machine, as he put it, civilization. Even in brilliantly dissecting the myth of this machine, Mumford fell back into that very same myth by seeming to implicitly accept the notion that ideas or works of art or discoveries are like tools in a toolbox, and can be meaningfully and without negative consequence used out of their original context: thoughts, ideas, and art as tools rather than as tapestries inextricably woven from and into a community of human and nonhuman neighbors. But discoveries, works of thought, and purposes that may work very well in the Great Plains may be harmful in the Pacific Northwest, and even more so in Hawai'i. To believe that this potential transposition is positive is the same old substitution of what is distant for what is near; if I really want to know how to live in Tu'nes, I should pay attention to Tu'nes.

There is another problem, though, that trumps all of these others. It has to do with a characteristic of our culture unshared even by other civilizations. It is our deeply- and transparently-held belief that there is really only one way to live, and that we are the one-and-only possessors of that way. It becomes our job then to propagate this way, by force when necessary, until there are no other ways to be. Far from being a loss, the eradication of these other ways to be, these other cultures, is instead an actual gain, since Western Civilization is the only way worth being anyway. We're doing ourselves a favor by getting rid of not only obstacles blocking our access to resources but reminders that other ways to be exist, allowing our fantasy to sidle that much closer to reality and we're doing the heathens a favor when we raise them from their degraded state to join the highest, most advanced, most developed state of society. If they don't want to join us, simple: we kill them. Another way to say all of this is that something grimly alchemical happens when we combine the arrogance of the dictionary definition, which holds our civilization superior to all other cultural forms; hyper-militarism, which allows civilization to expand and exploit essentially at will; and a belief, held even by such powerful and relentless critics of civilization as Lewis Mumford, in the desirability of cosmopolitanism, that is, the transposability of discoveries, values, modes of thought, and so on over time and space. The twentieth-century name for that grimly alchemical transmutation is genocide: the eradication of cultural difference, its sacrifice on the altar of the one true way, on the altar of the centralization of perception, the conversion of a multiplicity of moralities all dependent on location and circumstance to one morality based on the precepts of the ever-expanding machine, the surrender of individual perception (as through writing and through the conversion of that and other arts to consumables) to predigested perceptions, ideas, and values imposed by external authorities who with all their hearts—what's left of them—believe in, and who benefit by, the centralization of power. Ultimately, then, the story of our civilization is the story of the reduction of the world's tapestry of stories to only one story, the best story, the real story, the most advanced story, the most developed story, the story of the power and the glory that is Western Civilization.

Or maybe I should restate that. The story of our civilization is not the story of that reduction, but of its *attempted* reduction. Certainly it has already succeeded in eliminating many of the stories—the stories of great auks, passenger pigeons, many of the indigenous of Europe, North America, and Africa, the great herds of bison, the stories of free-flowing rivers—but it will never succeed in reducing all stories to one. The world won't let it. And, to the very best of my abilities, neither will I.

[1] *San Francisco Chronicle*, 9/13/01, 1.
[2] FAIR, Media, 9/17/01.
[3] FAIR, Media, 9/17/01.
[4] *Z Magazine*, July/August, 2000, 62.
[5] Edwards, 141.
[6] Drinnon, 96, citing Lipscomb, XI, 342-346, August 28, 1807.
[7] http://endgame.org/primer-facts.html.
[8] Of course it is manifestly true that those who work in the World Trade Center and especially the Pentagon do extraordinary harm—far more than mere frontline soldiers—to most of the humans and nonhumans in the world.
[9] See, for example, Lewis Mumford, Farley Mowat, RD Laing, and Derrick Jensen.
[10] Stannard, 4.
[11] Stannard, 4.
[12] Mumford, *Technics*, 186.
[13] Diamond, 1.
[14] Mumford, *Technics*, 186; awkwardness in original.
[15] Diamond, 4.
[16] Turner, 182.
[17] Fitzhugh, at Faust, 293.

e Fonz

Matt Roberts

They call him The Fonz. They call him The Fonz because he dresses like The Fonz. Shiny black penny loafers, a little scuffed from the pavement. Stiff, indigo denim jeans rolled up at the ankles to show off his sporty white socks. A matching white t-shirt. The brown leather bomber jacket, well worn in. And that cream he uses to slick back his hair. He doesn't look like The Fonz; he dresses like The Fonz.

I'm not a fancy bike with a clicking derailleur, taped up handlebars, skinny tires that can't take a thorn. I'm not a shiny Mongoose dirt bike with an excess of pads covering this bar and that. I'm your run of the mill bike. One speed. Coaster brake. Nice wide tires. No banana seat. No colorful streamers flowing from the grips. I'm not some little kid's bike. Not something to show off to the neighbors. But I'm good enough. Sometimes he takes me off pavement, down the dirt path between Avron and Irving, following the ditch that runs the length of the schoolyard.

He has me out of the garage today, away from the tools hanging on the wall and the paint sitting on the shelves. I'm grateful to be back out on the streets. It's really not a bad neighborhood. Lots of nice houses. Some big, some small. Sometimes we ride across the footbridge that crosses the canal, cruising up Wilson to the other bridge near the levee. We cross there and come down through that posh neighborhood of doctors and politicians. Past the house with the elevator for the kid with no arms. Past Pistol Pete's house. Sometimes you can see him at the door, signing posters for the kids. I bet he keeps a can of them, rolled up and in their clear, plastic bags, right there next to the door. The Fonz doesn't have one on his wall. Although we sometimes stop in the street in front of the house whenever we ride by.

We're out heading down 37th towards the footbridge. I can see the big house with the creepy circular window at the top floor, the Green Thing on my right. Sometimes I see boys trying to leap off of the Green Thing, to see if they can clear the bush that grows alongside it. Parrots nest in the palm tree in the adjacent yard. Their screeching can be heard for blocks, their bulky bodies on the telephone wires sticking out like sore green thumbs. We turn left and I can see the boys on Purdue Drive out throwing the football in the street. They are usually here. Smoking. Running. Yelling curse words. They drink beer out of cans with plastic sleeves that look like soda cans, and listen to music with lots of guitar solos. They sometimes shoot at each other with dull black plastic guns. *Crack-pop, crack-pop. Crack-pop.* But they are mostly out there throwing the football, trying hard not to drop their cigarettes from their mouths. There is the one they call Guffey. He has his shirt open, and has a habit of using his hand to sweep his long hair out of his face.

"Hey, Fonz," he says, sticking his thumb out. We come to a stop and are approached by Guffey; some of the other boys keep running. Others stop, smoke, and listen. The Fonz offers some conversation in response to Guffey's questions. He's asking us where we are going. He asks if The Fonz wants a beer. He asks if he can ride me. The Fonz has heard these questions before. From other boys. He won't give me up. Guffey continues asking questions. I've learned to tune these questions out. They are less questions than comments. Punctuated by laughter from him and the other boys.

I see a little boy at the curb. He's holding toys as if he is playing, but I know he is watching us. Always watching. I see you, little boy. What are you looking at? Go back about your business. Go play with your action figures. Nothing to see here.

The Fonz is stuttering. He is shaking his head. Maybe blushing. The girl question. Guffey has started his usual routine. Questions about "pussy" and "hand-jobs." Why do we come here? Why does The Fonz bring me here every time he sees them? It makes me angry. I want to crush them. I want to crush them all. I imagine The Fonz, without warning, lifting me in his hands and using me to smash their smart mouths. I hope that my frame's cold steel might catch a corner of bone on their soft heads, that an audible crack might be heard, a pop, and that the blood might then pour out slow like red paint on a cold day. Maybe just a tooth, jarred loose. The head spun away wildly in disbelief, jerking back with a hand at the chin, holding together the remains of a mouth freed of its pride. A dribble of spit, foam, and blood dropping onto that clean white button down shirt from the mall.

But that never happens. I am forced to wait patiently until The Fonz realizes that he can't let go of me, that they will never throw him the football, that he is not one of them. We slowly turn, and he pedals me away, Guffey shouting something at our back. We never turn left after these meetings. But right. Back down 37th Street, away from the footbridge, back home. He puts me in the garage. He can't leave me on the lawn. Someone will take me. Not because I am a thing of value to them, but because it would be funny to know that The Fonz would be looking for me. That he would be upset. That a man his age might cry and fume about his lost bike.

The shovel hanging against the wall on the peg rack tells me that my anger is misplaced. That I am not angry with the boys in the neighborhood, but rather that I am mad at myself. That I am embarrassed by the fact that I am the bike of a retarded man, that I do not appreciate The Fonz. That I need to learn to love myself. I've heard this before and have had enough. I lurch at the wall, falling away from the workbench, and clatter to the floor. And it is here that I will have to wait until The Fonz comes down from rocking in a ball on the floor of his own room, maybe tomorrow, maybe next week, to take me for yet another ride around the neighborhood. The cans of red paint sit silently on the shelves, saying nothing.

Dick Diamond and Harriet Welch

A Conversation

"Who's your audience? What's your market? How much will the screenplay be worth? How do we get Tom Cruise to play the lead, and will his schedule be free?"

[At this point, Dick Diamond and Harriet Welch, disobedient and dismayed, abruptly leave the library. Inside, a panel of publishers, editors and authors — spearheaded by the editor of *Colorado Review* — speak incessantly about analyzing markets and targeting consumers — calculations and cold capitalism concerned with the written word. Dick lights a cigarette and rubs his head. Harriet goes over and picks up the week's issue of the *Rocky Mountain Bullhorn*, and flips through the pages.]

Harry: Well, Dick, who woulda thunk a confused li'l indy rag like this would have lasted so long from hearing those people talk. It's kinda spooky. Is it all about making money?
Dick: At least *Matter* is out of debt again. That's something. When did books become such an industry?
Harry: Oh, it's been a gradual process of commoditization of ideas, spanning thousands of years. I mean before the press, everything was written down by priests, right? Only the select few were allowed to partake in the precious and inconsistent transcription of volumes. For a long time it has been the issue of who are the keepers of the words and what are they saying.
Dick: And where can you buy what they are saying?
Harry: BARNES AND NOBLE!
Dick: Ugghh.
Harry: But it's true. I mean we've had this conversation once or twice — the disparity between the worlds of independent and dependent publishing.
Dick: Ah, yes, dependent publishing, the world of big name publishers and big name authors and big name stores and big time sell sell sellers. One of your favorite soapboxes, eh, Harriet?
Harry: Well, hopefully, *Matter* and other indy publications like the *Bullhorn* enable a rupturing of this dependent model, by creating its own market, publishing itself, and constellating community through writing. It is a form of civil disobedience is it not? The chain of command is broken, the publishing is usurped. The writers and publishers partake in disobedience by creating new chains.
Dick: You don't even know how screwed we are Harriet. We are unbelievably screwed.
Harry: What?
Dick: Screwed! With a capital S, big time SCREWED! Do you remember the Mohammad Ali book at the publishing trade show? It was [indicates with hands three feet apart] this big. A big ole book of a big time celebrity and it sold for thousands and thousands of dollars. Who needs that? Where is that getting us?

I've said it before and I'll say it again: we're the muscle flexing of the publishing ecosystem and... what did I say last time—it was really good.

Harry: Listen grasshopper, that all sounds fine and dandy, but if we were really concerned with the ecosystem, then we would publish online instead of on paper.

Dick: What are you saying Harry? I can't believe what you are saying! You saw the memo I sent you last week?

Harry: What are you talking about?

Dick: That email entitled MEMO ON THE STARK REALITY: THE PAPERLESS FUTURE OF THE INTERNET IS A SHAM OF UNFATHOMABLE PROPORTIONS SIMPLY BECAUSE OF THIS SIMPLE FACT: WE USE MORE PAPER THAN WE DID BEFORE THE INTERNET WAS INVENTED.

Harry: I never got it.

Dick: Lost in space. Nuf said. Give me a cigarette.

Harry: But Dick, you are hedging the issue of disobedience again. It is the public's willingness to partake in reading and supporting unsanctioned publications which makes the whole rupturing of said system possible.

Dick: You're loosing me.

Harry: I'm *loosing* you? Are you drunk? What I mean is *Matter* is not solely contingent upon the devotion of Todd Simmons and its editors. Let us return to that being out of debt thing. If the community of Fort Collins did not go to coffee shops and buy *Matter* then it wouldn't go on. It is the community's willingness to disobey sanctioned locations of book retail, turning instead to their local coffee-fix places for its literary needs.

Dick: Where are you going?

Harry: Home.

Dick: No, I mean with your point?

Harry: My point? I will not comment on the phallic nature of your phrasing.

Dick: It's not my fault my mother named me Dick. It was her act of creation. Get off your soap box, Lucy.

Harry: Shit man, I was only kidding. How else do we rupture the system?

Dick: What is it, a boil? Take advice from the gypsies: Once you plug into the system, the meters start running. *Matter* is dependent my dear friend, but in a critical mass sort of way, dependent upon the disobedient community committed to supporting it. Hey, what time is the critical mass bicycle ride anyway?

Harry: 5:30 pm, every last Friday of the month, at the oval on campus.

Dick: What was that?

Harry: 5:30 pm, every last Friday of the month, at the oval on campus.

Dick: Right, gotta gotta get to it.

Harry: Why aren't we talking about windmills?

Dick: I forgot.

Harry: Oh.

Turning around after one of my missed turns, some invisible creature hisses at me from the dark roadside. Though later I would be assured by **local experts** that it was most likely a **raccoon**, in the moment I am convinced I have scared a **bobcat** or some other oversized wild cat. For about a quarter mile I am **highly motivated**.

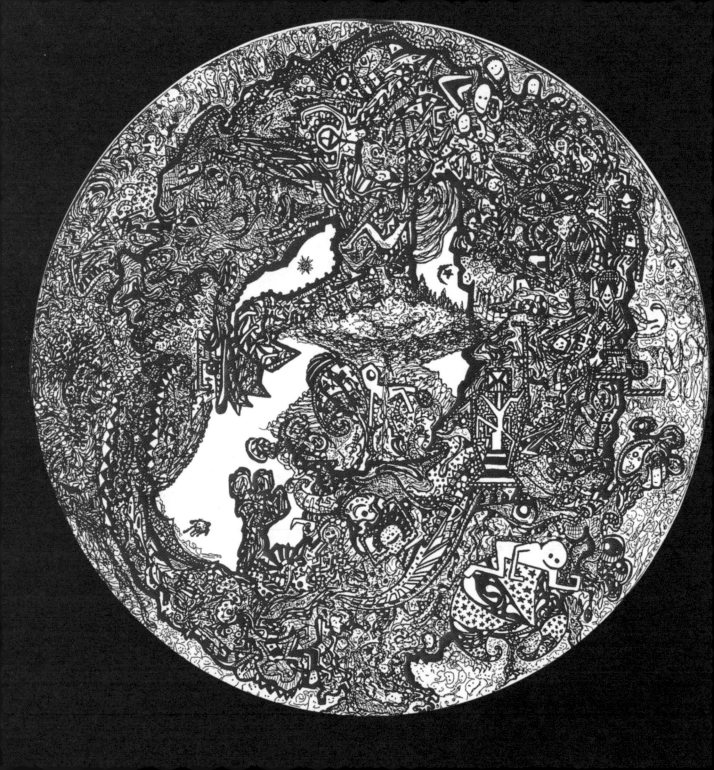

Laura Mullen

Dedicated (Dictated)

All that needs to Almost blind   All that needs   Before movement   As the word happens   Pattern
        Of distance   Oceans continuous see   All that needs   To know   What would a
clarity between What world   As happens   And nothing else subject   To him speak   "When I
praise...don't think..."   It's just I won't see   Fell into what I was bade   Only justify
        Although moving   Fictive presence   Trying to The connection   Loose the
whole   Time   Syntactically alone   White as my absolute dreaming Rich with ice   Was bade
        Speak   "I sank with"   The voice sounds   Goodbye "And we can't see"   Lost or In the
silences   Remembering   "Swim in water Eat black cookies"   Raw and ghostly   In
terrible cold   The objects which   Do not see   Themselves   Ingesting   What will not
happen Old slow infinite exposure   Fear   Fear tricking   The world   But she doesn't exist
        Having tongued away   The white   Into the mmmmmmmoon   She   Repetition
        When the poem Rival   Evil somehow Between Bruised indice   The broken   Hear them hiss
whisper Accurate observe   Other Eye accurate   Swallows broken   Blackness as an eye
        Light caws or   To shore   Late   And cold   "I wonder what I thought"   Splash
with sleep   Dreaming   Time does not finish   In the empty   Funhouse just as   Cold as
we   Lights out   This much   Time does   Not finish what I   Dreaming   Kept a
house by the side   Love cold   No realer   On the old amusement pier   The seagulls go
over   Where all wheel keen   Believe birds

Robert Urquhart

Return Dust to Stone

so they return swirling white amid black for a season

that was the wind given its voice changed by morning
though never enough taken in to recount it all the passage
to a new time

for whom rain the water courses filling a voice from
nowhere I will stay to watch them grow now who said

return dust to stone and the tiny creatures falling dead
through shallow waters

in darkness movement to take on the horizon's outline

so they can return

said the one left behind

nothing more to be found

land and pushed away soft in the distance to make land fall
waiting to see what will travel to show the road lying in wait
she did not think of the lightening as originating elsewhere
and all things withdraw to an immense distance not gone but
very far away beyond an invisible perimeter but recognizable
each one when color must stand in for touch and taste and smell
silent but still from here

irregular to postpone the final balance the letter unintended sent
out across the world so that something else can happen engulfing
the event over before it started others walk that path from here to
there making just these turns pausing for a gap in the traffic to cross
quickly lightly as if nothing depended on being in that place now
and saw the sun go behind the cloud and measured out the steps to
its return when that lamp post casts its shadow again come to nothing
hold it there suspended

that could contain such a reversal of all understanding without
a movement in the scene before the eyes each stone each branch
each shadow in place and the small cloud evaporating in the sun
in an infinity of reductions will be enough to guard the sanctum
of change for the world to continue without so distant a revolution
it must be somewhere else they turned north not knowing the extent
of the broken land in so strong a wind that it was hard to see skirting
the decision

impossible in the street at this time of day to keep an eye on the one
half a block ahead past all those shifting others distinguishable as a
shape moving in that way a changing surface bearing to the resisting
air she recognized that clearly there a line straight through in mid stride
head to toe just once before the corner is the beginning of everywhere
else

stand

carve

cloud

fold   then

pass

down

still

fly

near

drift   clearing

curl

wind

fall

hold

door

last

dry

way

heard

where

floor

found

hand

send

talk

land

field

bring

edge

work

seen

sound

climb

glide

gone

curve

line

wall

veil

fade

bright

stone

dust

flood

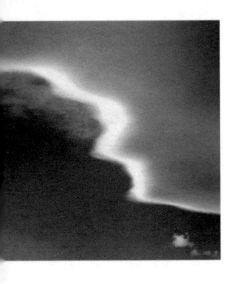  

Joan Marsan

Clastic

Sometimes it's knowledge that matters,
or direction and the map and compass that help you find it.

But here, water is the most important thing
you'll take with you. There's not much of it

in the Mojave, just what you bring on your back,
although liquid alone is what bored the deep pockets,

handholds and footholds, in these canyon walls of sandstone
so solid they could be confused for quartzite

pressed firm under its own weight.
This water you'll carry isn't nearly that heavy,

each gallon a little more than eight pounds,
though after a few miles it might feel like eight hundred.

Still, that's nothing compared to the weight
of what you left behind when you came to this desert,

what made your heart immobile as these iron-stained cliffs
that only the wind, rare rain and scorching heat can break
apart,

shape into something new.

IT'S A
NOMAD
NOMAD
WORLD

Todd
Simmons

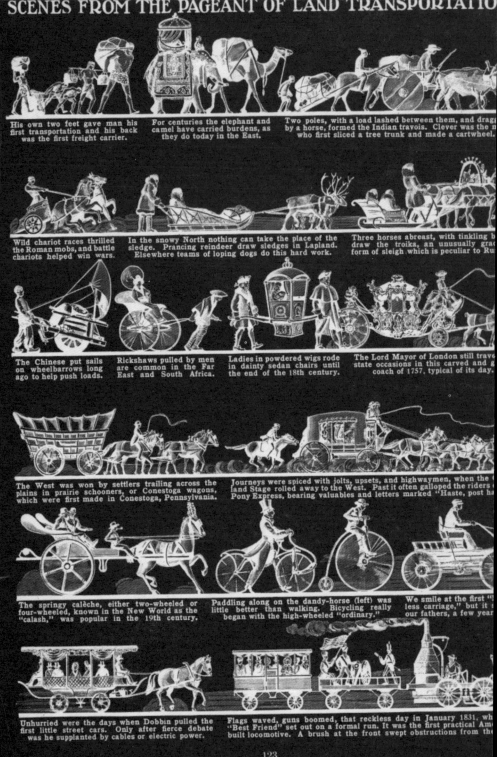

His own two feet gave man his first transportation and his back was the first freight carrier.

For centuries the elephant and camel have carried burdens, as they do today in the Far East.

Two poles, with a load lashed between them, and drag by a horse, formed the Indian travois. Clever was the who first sliced a tree trunk and made a cartwheel.

Wild chariot races thrilled the Roman mobs, and battle chariots helped win wars.

In the snowy North nothing can take the place of the sledge. Prancing reindeer draw sledges in Lapland. Elsewhere teams of loping dogs do this hard work.

Three horses abreast, with tinkling b draw the troika, an unusually grac form of sleigh which is peculiar to Ru

The Chinese put sails on wheelbarrows long ago to help push loads.

Rickshaws pulled by men are common in the Far East and South Africa.

Ladies in powdered wigs rode in dainty sedan chairs until the end of the 18th century.

The Lord Mayor of London still trave state occasions in this carved and g coach of 1757, typical of its day.

The West was won by settlers trailing across the plains in prairie schooners, or Conestoga wagons, which were first made in Conestoga, Pennsylvania.

Journeys were spiced with jolts, upsets, and highwaymen, when the land Stage rolled away to the West. Past it often galloped the riders Pony Express, bearing valuables and letters marked "Haste, post ha

The springy calèche, either two-wheeled or four-wheeled, known in the New World as the "calash," was popular in the 19th century.

Paddling along on the dandy-horse (left) was little better than walking. Bicycling really began with the high-wheeled "ordinary."

We smile at the first "less carriage," but it our fathers, a few year

Unhurried were the days when Dobbin pulled the first little street cars. Only after fierce debate was he supplanted by cables or electric power.

Flags waved, guns boomed, that reckless day in January 1831, wh "Best Friend" set out on a formal run. It was the first practical Am built locomotive. A brush at the front swept obstructions from th

"Our travels are not over. However, the day has come down and we all stop moving to eat. The feast is laid out before us. Delicacies are cut and open, bleeding and oozing and steaming. Everyone wears a strangely placed smile as we nod in agreement at our good fortune. This feast took a long time to prepare, but we are sure we can finish it off quickly and move on somewhere else. I look around and see that everyone is ravenous and excited, ready to go. We have not agreed on a common prayer to say, so we say nothing out loud, though I'm sure we're all rattling off all sorts of mantras and songs and jokes and little ditties in our heads — rub a dub dub, thanks for the grub, yeah God…We nod to each other, lick our lips, and dig in."
— Sigurd O' Flanigan, 1928, *Travels Unencumbered*

What do nomads do? Nomads move. Nomads pull up stakes to strike again at the horizon, always seeking that which sustains them. You can't say nomad without thinking movement, but nomads will often return to the same place, trusting that sustenance awaits. In an irrational and intuitive way, nomads seem to pay more attention to the world, letting go of what seems unnecessary.

Nature's theme song is, of course, "(I Can't Get No) Satisfaction." We wake up each day to see a new part of the world thanks to nature's one steady question: What works best? Nature is never satisfied, or how about this: nature is satisfied completely in each moment, but only in each moment, and only once that way. Nature thinks: is there anything better than now, and tomorrow will ask the same question when everything is different from now. As part of nature, have we realized we are sitting on all the background and decoration that's us? All we see is this orbiting body, searching always for that magical place where space and time fit. We won't move forward, not towards survival or happiness or fulfillment, unless we keep alert to all our ridiculous divisions, the long stretches of mesmerizing action, the holidays, the days spent staring at wheels in sheer delight and frustration, the battles of burning out or burning up — of going to the depths, the very epitome of *internomadism*, then coming back to the surface, the stretched plane of diversity and complexity, ready to give to the resistance of the map, the white sheet, the stain, the music made by spinning feet and wrenched hands. [This is how a nomad talks.]

Check your feet; they itch and groan to move. Check your mind; it screams from thought to thought, moving like any healthy nomad. Your whole being is a survival yardstick, and we are all nomads on some level, always seeking out — whether physically, intellectually, emotionally — that which sustains us. Moving is harsh and illiterate and you must be completely obsessive with genealogies. You get to learn all about renouncing, and what it means to have faith. Being constructed in one place, I wouldn't trust a short definition of survival. It must be simple, profound, off-kilter, a ladder at the dead-end wall, a bullhorn in the time of need, a thief, a shape-shifter. It must be a money making machine, for some. A win-win situation for others. A win-win-lose-lose-win-lose ad nauseam for most. Our great big brains just can't seem to keep up with survival. All the while time is continuously clipping our wings, and watching us fall, and soaring at us as the bells signal that everything is as it should be. We move through stages, reach pinnacles, shout, "This is it" and then wander aimlessly again, searching for something else.

My father was a truck driver.

He started driving late one night over thirty years ago. Along with my mother he had a new family to support; living in a culture increasingly bent on speed and addicted to oil, it seemed a good way to make a living, if only for a short while. He was employed for seventeen years with the same company, secure, reasonably content though often tired from working long, strange hours. Seventeen years in a cycle of stability that shifted his days to nights and nights to days, putting in endless miles with crippled, arthritic hands.

One day out of nowhere, the company my father worked for was bought up or bought out or went broke and my father was out of work. He found work, after a time, once again behind the wheel. He drove trucks for another thirteen years, rising ever earlier, until he really didn't rise from sleep, but was just a constant stumbling around from being tired from one day's work to being ready for the next day's work.

In thirty years of driving trucks, my father delivered millions of pounds of goods, powered by our culture's addiction to oil. My father will readily admit that his job revolved largely around convenience—what we interpreted as survival for our family, and for those he delivered goods to and for. At first he delivered large-scale appliances, such as refrigerators and dishwashers, and then it was bread. Since my father retired, he has vacated his space in the economy. A twenty-three year old man straight out of driving school has filled his space, eager to have a full-time job, eager to have the power afforded by eighteen wheels, eager to survive. The system continues because new participants agree to its conditions. Quite simply, if my father's space hadn't been filled, wouldn't we learn to flour the board and pound the dough ourselves? What if we left some of these attempts at survival behind that rely on absurd expressions of love, in this case our love for convenience driven by love of oil? There is nothing wrong with loving oil, thinking of the process of oil being made, of all the things that made oil; and I intend no disrespect for those who made it possible for us to survive—without the hard work of the past, we would be nowhere, or at least not here. But our love for convenience and oil has lead to senseless wars, to humans who cannot do for themselves, to pollution, to dying jobs and towns, SUV's, embargos, wrecked cargo tankers, dying seals and ghastly different skies to look at. It's a little like saying trash bags are empty unless filled. Our love for convenience powered by oil took a dive and hell is conjured.

The world as nomad. I think if someone could see clearly enough, this is surely what the world must look like, the world as nomad: always moving but coming back around: each moment consumed wholly, turned into something new. What are the things in life to hold onto, with all this moving and shifting and consuming continuously? I would like to think this ground under our feet, but I don't see the attraction of ruining it for convenience's sake. Surely not this ground under our feet, as we are all scurrying around like rats as far as I can see. Surely not these days, which we tick off the calendar quick as they come. These moments? Can we hold onto these moments? These brief flashes that play continuously whether we like it or not? Surely we can't hold onto these possessions of ours. Natural disasters teach us something about what to hold onto. Natural disasters move us forward, push us into tunnel vision about survival, wrapped up as we are in a world of convenience. Natural disasters are *disasters* for some, and windfall for others. Who wins: and who loses: and who is holding the whistle, signaling finality? I look to both sides and resist decisions, concentrating only on survival. This is not to say I am the worst of the greedy human lot: I want the trees to make it too; I want wolves and grizzly bears to roam everywhere again; and I want the buffalo back (if only to make hiking in Kansas more exciting). I take seriously what Jackson Pollock used to scream, "What're you involved in?"

Full on now gallops the nomadic tendency: searching and journeying versus staying put: being still geared towards survival: that pull of life: the pull of the will to live: a force reckoned with only by moving. Some say turn off the switch, our eyes need a rest. Turn off the switch and we'll get off this funny merry-go-round and sit down on the ground and look around for once, see what is going on. We live in a world of circles. If we are not careful to change direction or stop we'll end up where we started. Of course we can walk straight lines, follow grids, and go up or down.

It's easy to ignore the map. One flip of the wrist sends it over the shoulder and the Earth is undiscovered once again. The important part of living is attending to what is not known. This might be beside the point, but do we know our neighbors, the names of the plants growing on the side of the road or the streak of dark green trees creeping up the mountain, the way to move wheels without destroying everything? Do we know the word for the wind at our back (Chinook?) or the birds streaking overhead? It's a nomad *nomad* world, one we rush into as we scream behind us for others to hold up the flashlight. We hardly see anything, and what we do see is like the vibrant, shimmering, seemingly empty space created when a wheel spins fast enough. It is these spaces we see or want to fit into—something not fully visible, but we believe to be there. Call it a ghost wheel if you will. Faith is placed in spaces needing filled, and a new expression of life is produced.

We are all case studies in nomadism, wandering this way and that, tumultuously ascending and descending, creating and destroying, arriving and loving and confusing love with leaving, but never paying enough attention to where we are and — Foolish Earth! — we could've killed you a thousand times had we been able to live without you.

This is what the world tells us: we're all going to die, stand back, stay still, this is all-too-funny, toy with some resistance, explore the mysteries, find friction, be passionate, keep moving.

Sue Ring deRosset

America, Roaring

Sometime
in the sigh of the night
as we wait for the scared trees to breathe
ask me about that time I drove through Kansas
and heard America.

Not as He was as a newborn —
we've all heard His first spank of stone
and the wail of inland sea,
the slide of ice along his spine.

And not as He was as a child —
with His first cry of crickets
and cottonwood leaves;
His sentence of badger claws
in a prairie dog town;
the spitty scritch as a pronghorn licks
her new twitching kid; the drip, drip
as a heron lifts her bill
from the still shallows of a
shadowed pond at dawn.
Or the smooth language
of flatrock moccasins,
nighthawk stories,
buffalo song.

But as He is now,

the three hundred year old adolescent.
He grows so fast. He eats too much. His mouth is
always open, and he belches, yells, and roars:
> the mechanical screaming of eighteen wheels
> going ninety on I-70. The bang of
> corrugated metal flapping off the gas station roof
> during a dust storm. The man in the pick-up
> by the pump (kerCHUNK kerCHUNK), "You
> fucking bitch!" and his companion, "But honey I -"
And, in the field behind the grasshopper afternoon,
bullets rive the sage, strike like thunder. A small body
hits the earth with a small thud, and forever
bleeds the ground a prairie-dog red.

Sometime
when the night lies still and dark
as a house abandoned, and the fever'd
prairie is quiet, and the owls are unafraid
to settle their feathers on a branch above us,
ask me about our trip across America,
that time I heard the throat
of Kansas wailing through a sunflower
farm; I have to tell
someone what I heard.
But I'm afraid that none will listen, no one
can even hear; I myself in my fourth decade,
facing the stage where the headbanging
heavy metal band of humanity is screaming into
the microphones, I am slowly going
deaf

as grass.

Ask me. Ask me
before I plumb forget. Because
I don't want to forget the song of

the meadowlark, how her fluting music
floats like a thread across the penstemmon
and primrose in the tummy of our country.
I don't want to forget what the wind sounds like
as it brushes up against the cheeks of the feral
sunflowers and grooms the skin of the pond
whiskered with bulrushes.

Let's turn off the lights, the tee-vee, the stereo,
and leave our fuming cars,
ditch them where the magpies
will pick them clean and hoard the shiny things.
Exhale with the chokecherry and ash as they relax
their massive old shoulders and hard-axed boles,
and come sit beneath the evening owls,
and listen for a while, and pray now
that our bullying boy comes finally home,
that our rowdy loud teenager
grows up.

Gary Wockner

Hideaway

The cabin faces due east, into the morning sun, with a view beyond. It sits on a little rise in the granite outcrops overlooking Lake Hiawatha. As I approach the front deck, the morning light hits the log siding and gives off a warm, yellow glow. Four large ponderosa pines slightly shield my view of the lake. Off to the right a small group of aspen twinkle their fall colors near a little stream. The sky is brilliantly blue, the water likewise, and the bright green pines and mountain scenery beyond fitting each other like a puzzle.

As I ease the screen door open and walk through the front door, I notice an antique wood cook stove. Its black-and-chrome front is scalded with age and use, and several pans and metal spatulas are hung on the wall behind it. To its left is a small pile of split pine, just the right size to fit in the firebox. In front of the cook stove and filling the main room of the cabin is a huge, circular, braided-rag rug. The rags are intermixed cream, pale green, and tan and all have a slight yellow glow reflecting from the log beams that run across the ceiling.

To the left, circling around the other end of the rug, is a long, low couch. In front of the couch is a large picture window which looks out across the deck and over the water. I walk over and sit down and it is immediately obvious that the cabin's builder had this view in mind. The picture window is lower than normal so that even when reclining on the couch I can see the sparkling water in the late-morning sun.

Beyond the lake, the forest rises up and spreads over the mountains, the sky an unending cacophony of clouds and sun-streaks. About an hour northwest of Fort Collins, Colorado, up near the Wyoming border, this cabin is in the tiny village of Red Feather Lakes. The area around the village sits in a park-like setting at 8,000 feet of elevation surrounded by a million acres of national forest. Across the lake and into the hills beyond are mounded granite outcrops stretching for miles in each direction. Snow-capped peaks are visible in two directions. Massive pine-covered mountains create a carpet of green all around.

It's a tranquil spot, exactly what I've been looking for. The cares of the modern world, though only an hour away, feel ten-times farther. Anyone, I think, could lose their troubles and soothe their soul sitting on this cabin's deck. And after talking to the real estate agent that came along with me today, I find out that the man who built this place was trying to do just that.

Longmont, Colorado is only about two hours south of Red Feather Lakes, but the ten miles that separates Longmont from the mountains feel more like two-hundred miles as I enter town. It's the weekend after my visit to the cabin, and I've come here to meet the cabin's owner, Ronald Jameson. The realtor up in Red Feather was very friendly but couldn't answer some of my questions about the cabin. Further, as the realtor talked, Ron's story drew me in.

On the phone, Ron sounded old and not very healthy, but friendly. As the realtor predicted, Ron was happy to get together for a visit. "Sure, be glad to talk," Ron said in a bright but raspy voice. "I have pictures that I took while I built the place." As he gave me directions to his house, he coughed a little. "2:00, Saturday," he said.

When I drive up to Ron's house, the contrast between his mountain cabin and his year-round home are dramatic. Here in Longmont, Ron lives in a plain suburban ranch house on a wide city lot. Three deciduous trees sit in his yard but don't obscure the new cookie-cutter subdivision at the end of the street.

Ron opens his front door and limps out to greet me on this fine fall day. He's wearing green work pants and a white t-shirt and holds a cane in his left hand. At about five-feet-eight and a little stooped over, his thin body looks frail and delicate. He's very old, which dampens my earlier enthusiasm. I wonder if I'm intruding too much or just being nosey where I shouldn't. As he approaches, his wide smile sets me at ease. Wire-rim glasses cover his glistening blue eyes as he reaches out his hand. The creases in his face are twirled roundabout into smiling circles.

After we shake hands and exchange greetings, I look down at his cane. He notices my gaze. "Lost my leg two years ago. Diabetes," he says, smiling. "This one's wooden." And then he leans over with his right hand and knocks two times on his left leg about midway down his thigh. He smiles as his head bobs back up. I smile back.

As we enter the house, I'm greeted by Shirley, Ron's wife. She's not quite as old, and a little rounder. She, too, has wire-rim glasses hiding blue eyes, and she quickly takes my jacket and places it on the living room couch. The furniture and all the wall-hangings remind of my granddad's house of thirty years ago. Everything is old and slightly yellowed, and there's a certain smell, not a bad smell, but a distinct smell of doors and windows shut and people aging.

"You're interested in the cabin?" Shirley asks, also smiling.

"Yeah. I was up there last week and spoke with John, your realtor," I say. "Quite a place. Hope you don't mind me coming down to look at pictures and ask a few questions?"

"Not at all," she says. "A beautiful spot up there. We're going to miss it. Ron knows every board and every nail."

Beside the couch is a card table with a photo album spread out on top. Above the album sit two loose pictures. In one I can see the outline of a submarine. Shirley motions me over to the card table where Ron has already sat down and started narrating.

The photo album takes us back to Red Feather Lakes in 1948. Ron took a sequence of black-and-white pictures as he was building the cabin, the first of which shows the empty lot. Several stakes with white flags outline the building site. The next photo shows the foundation being laid, and then the flooring and framing as the photos continue. The original ponderosa pine logs that Ron used for the corner posts and ceiling joists are lying on the ground beside the cabin. "I cut them up by Beaver Meadows," Ron says. "Used to be some pretty big trees up there. Most of them were logged out right after the war."

On the next few pages, the cabin's interior takes shape, and it is here where Ron's descriptions become more animated. He was a finish carpenter for most of his life, a cabinet maker in his later years. As he describes the woodwork and kitchen cabinets in the photos, I glance over my shoulder through his living room and see similar pine cabinets in his Longmont kitchen.

"Nice work," I say as he points through the photos.

"Thanks," he says. "I was young back then. Had a lot of energy."

As we're looking through the photos, I ask a few basic questions about the cabin—plumbing, septic tank, wiring, etc. Ron knows the exact history of each. The cabin had an outhouse up until 1980 which still stands right behind it. He retired in 1980 and with his carpenter's pension he put in indoor plumbing. Then he and Shirley started spending all summer up there until about 1992.

"Last twelve years, me and Shirley haven't got up there much. Health, you know," he says. "I have two daughters. One in Los Angeles and one in Denver. But they have families and everybody's busy. We all talked about it, and decided to sell the place." As he says this, he looks up at me. His expression is frank and unassuming.

We talk a little more about the cabin, and then I ask a few questions about the history of Red Feather Lakes. Ron launches into a series of stories about people and property and buildings. He stops to cough every few minutes as we talk, and his eyes get a little red after each fit of coughing. Still, his energy seems high and I try to garner what I can from his words. His house is quiet, and though his voice is soft, his words are strong.

A few minutes later, I point back to the card table to the loose photos above the album. "What about that submarine," I ask. "The realtor said you had quite a story there," I say.

"Well, I don't know about that," he says slowly, losing his animation. He leans over and grabs the photos.

He clears his throat. "These were my guys." He hands me the picture. "That was taken when we shipped out. Maryland. We were green. Didn't know nothing."

The black-and-white picture in my hands shows a dozens guys standing on top of a submarine in a dock, all of them dressed smartly in Navy uniforms. The faces are dramatically young. "I'm right there," says Ron pointing to a blurry face.

"Here's another shot." He hands me the second picture. "Close up. That was on a good day, before the Bulge. I'm right there." His finger is pointing to the left-most man of a group of six standing on top of the submarine out in the open ocean. "That's in the North Sea. September, '44. The Bulge started in mid-December. That's when Hitler went crazy."

'The Bulge' Ron is referring to is the Battle of the Bulge. When I was up in Red Feather last weekend, the realtor told me a bit of Ron's story and so I spent a little time reading about the battle before I came down here.

The Battle of the Bulge lasted from December 16, 1944 to January 28, 1945 and was the largest U.S. land battle of World War II. More than a million men fought in it including 600,000 Germans, 500,000 Americans, and 55,000 British. Six weeks later when the battle was over the casualties were as follows: 81,000 U.S. with 19,000 killed, 1400 British with 200 killed, and 100,000 Germans killed, wounded or captured.

Prior to the battle, in late 1944, Germany was clearly losing the war. The Russian Red Army was steadily closing in on the Eastern front while German cities were being devastated by intense American bombing. The Italian peninsula had been captured and liberated, and the Allied armies were advancing rapidly through France. Hitler knew the end was near if the Allied advance wasn't slowed. He came up with a plan to launch a major last-ditch offensive on the Western front. Though his advisors thought the plan ridiculous, Hitler ordered it anyway.

Although most of the battle was on land in Belgium, Germany, and France, a portion of the battle took place in the North Sea and the English Channel. Via those water passages, American and British forces re-supplied troops in the European mainland. Beyond supplies, thousands of troops were shipped over to reinforce the mainland fighters over the six-week battle.

The Germans patrolled the supply routes with U-Boats and submarines. Several Allied ships were sunk including the U.S.S. Leopoldville on Christmas Eve, 1944, in which 980 Americans died in the English Channel. Ron's submarine, the U.S.S. Admiralty, and other American ships tried to protect the Channel and the supply routes.

"We were in constant battle for over a month," Ron says while looking down at the photo. "On the surface, the Germans were throwing depth charges down at us, and underwater their subs were firing torpedoes at us. We fired back. Took out a few, too.

"About mid-January, things were getting ugly. We'd had U-Boats throwing charges at us for several days and all the guys were getting crazy from the noise and stress. Then a German sub started following us and shot several torpedoes. We heard a couple hiss by.

"I was working about mid-way back in the sub with eight other guys and every few minutes we'd hear, 'Charges!' over the horn. And everybody would just freeze. Ten seconds, maybe twenty would go by. Just waiting to see if we'd die. Sitting ducks. Nothing we could do. Then the explosion would hit.

"The bomb would knock you off your feet and reverberate and echo so loud it would make you vomit and cry from the pain in your head. The guys were going crazy, shell-shocked."

Ron's voice is getting a little raspy and he coughs a little. The lines in his face are now long and straight. And then he continues, "When I was younger, in high school, me and my dad used to go up to Red Feather hunting in the fall. I always liked it up there," he says. "During those last few days of the Bulge, I couldn't stop thinking about it. Complete opposite places.

"At one point after several depth charges hit around us, I was laying on the belly of the sub with all my crewmates. Some of the guys were crying or praying. Others were calling out for their moms and girlfriends. I was just squeezing my guts and gritting my teeth. And then after awhile I had kind of a vision and perfectly clear thought. 'If I ever get out of here,' I said to myself, 'I'm going to build a cabin in Red Feather Lakes.'" Ron looked up at me again as I met his eyes.

"Did, too," he said matter-of-fact, smiling.

"Yes," I said.

"War will make your head spin," he continued, "like a wheel, around and around. That little cabin seemed to stop the spinning."

A few days later I drive back up to Red Feather Lakes to take another look at the cabin. About three inches of snow fell the day before, and though the paved roads are clear, the fields and forest are mottled white, brown, and green. Off the paved highway, the road turns to dirt and gravel and now mud with the snow. My truck tires spin slightly as I turn onto the small two-track road winding around the lake.

Though I'm here by myself, the realtor gave me the combination to the key-lock on the front door so I could look around a bit more. The sun is back out after yesterday's snow and the air sparkles. A slight breeze blows from the west bringing the roof's snow onto the deck. Looking at the roof, I see the beginning of a small cornice that will eventually grow and hold form well into spring.

I look around for several of the details Ron told me about. The outhouse in back still stands with the little half-moon slit in the door. The logs that run though the ceiling and stand under the front deck hardly show their fifty-six years of age. And the view from the deck across the lake is still picture perfect.

An intense quietness permeates the air as I look around. The world does indeed seem to stop spinning. Nature, at least today, is benevolent and nurturing. That Ron could soothe his soul here does not surprise me. And that nature could do that for any of us seems certain, too.

Carol Deering

Somewhere West of Laramie

Sun blinds the fractured
windshield. Cloistered within,
all music holds its breath.
The steering wheel poses
at awkward angles,
a medal for bravery, unwavering
against the blue beyond.

That night we spun 180,
black ice, and then black eye.
Time split and looked down crooked,
as we wriggled from windows
and watched a wheel set course
for a canyon filled with stars.

Wanton grasses lean
from the hollows of old tires.
This warrior has run its gallons,
rolled to landscape rubble,
now home to spikes
where snakes and packrats worship
and men with wrenches prey.

Erin Morrill

Pave

In that the lines of your face could be
bypassed via garage entrances and turning
the knob of the unlocked, I understood the attention
span of the line length as not being

conducive. To wind in the string to
the "forked tail thing" without forgetting how to write
how it went down — arbitrarily
insisting upon suggesting such things

like a body blundering, under "not enough"
circumstances, you calling finally to tell me I had
gotten your attention. How clear you made it
with, "you're an asshole; I can't believe you did that."

But I did not hear. I was far off, on a bus in southern Brasil
catching strands of "unconscious attacks the enemy"
not chasing this fibrous and binding ball of you
through some dusty fields, recalling *atencao*

or how I can at times still speak Portuguese and yet never write
how it went down —
the chicken or the word for
chicken, in Portuguese, lost to me. You

and your "asshole" mentality, wholly dictated
by the busting of hinges from too long...
not thru with you, a badly set bone
needing to be re-broken

                    for alignment,

                                  you

recoiled.
        I only meant for it to go so far
    across the page, then turn

                                    back on itself

          clipping its own
tail
                    "unconscious attacks, the enemy"

[*galinha*]

to assume that it could be unwound again
and return
      temperate, in memory.

(We left in rotations
so that [no one will know] us together.) Fifteen miles
an hour, the flip flop looses itself
from foot, a brake is made of knee.

                                        vai voltar

reparations: pace of double treadled wooden spokes and frame
                    breathing into its even thump with the ground
                    oil to quiet the incessant squeaking

reasons not to love lover #17
1) "crackhead"
2) ex-wife
3) likes to get spun

"what are you?"

                        madly written

                                                      fibers
coil about themselves as they still into one strand

rash of road, ridden rash
bearing tattooed cross section
(surgical scrub of asphalt
removal)   *bearing down. out. away.*

silk is for a skilled spinner, as it slips
from the hands so quickly; color of water lilies, slick and unwet

4) "the cricket customer you called is
    unavailable"
5) alleged drug busts
6) "love's an insect"
7) his one true love (see 1)

going too fast or didn't correct course fast enough... twisting the facts

sound bytes as breadcrumbs transposed into blood trail
spokes one thru thirty-six should have connoted wholeness

re-territorialization: lover # 16's house
                            post scene of the accident
                            littered with wet red dots, defiled

                    as mesmas que as estrellas

between the maidens, the orifice, along the edge of the many hooked flyer, a twist
as it curls about the bobbin, spun

stitches weren't required, no skin to pull together
merely bandages to contain

the re-opened wound, having to
again under go the removal of surfaced black silt
scars, marking time, "the doctor
will be with you momentarily"
(through the third story window
an aleatoric ocean recedes and
reconvenes)

a touch of the knee, to return, in purpled flesh, memory
(peel back the skin to find...
                        what?

its embedded particles; taking road with me

ownership: *my* bloodstained pavement, "still there"

Claire Petersky

Get Off the Fucking Road

There may be a day while you are riding your bike when a motorist passes you, and calls out, "Get off the fucking road!" You may be puzzled. What do these words mean? The key to understanding this motorist's cry is to realize that the road does not copulate with itself. Rather, it is you who is partnered with the road.

Have you not had a day out on your bike, and there is the road before you, warm and inviting? It feels good, it smells good, it almost seems to taste good to be on it. Some days you start out eager, knowing what lies ahead. Other days you start out a little reluctantly—surely you have better things to do—clean the house, mow the lawn—but here you are anyway, your bike and the road together, and after a little bit you know its going to be a good time.

There are days when you dominate the road. It does your bidding. You groove on your control. There are other days when the road is your master. You submit to its demands. You get a perverted pleasure from the pain of your burning legs, your oxygen-starved lungs screaming for air. In any of these instances, though, you with your bike, and the road, are lovers. The term, "get off" as we all know, is a slang term that means to "derive pleasure". Thus, the encouraging, if crude, words, "Get off the fucking road" can be understood as "Enjoy yourself as you and the road make beautiful love together".

To take this a step further—in many mystical traditions, the physical act of love is understood as a metaphor for the spiritual union of human with the Divine. Can you ride as if you and the Road are One?

The mudra of the single upraised digit is a reminder of this oneness: unity in Christ Consciousness, being at one with the Tao, La illaha Il' Allah, Adonai Echad. Thus, when someone makes this gesture at you, you should understand that they are wishing you the experience of this ecstatic union.

The horn that is honked as the mudra is made is a meditation bell. Like a church bell, like the call of the muezzin's voice, it calls you into this sacred space of union, of you, your bike, and the road, as One.

Thus, when the motorist honks his horn, raises the single digit, and makes his sincere invocation, you have but one response: to smile, to wave, and return to The Joy of Riding your bike.

Ian Tyson

Preface to the Disco Poems

To write a poem today one requires a machine. In the past metaphors might have worked along with a number of other gimmicks enabling the reader to reduce difference within the poem in order to grasp some arbitrarily abstract theme. Instead of the reduction of difference why not a machine that produces a way into life? In this case the machine is disco, or rather house music, a sped up disco, or as DJ Frankie Knuckles said *disco's revenge*. They call a disco beat *four to the floor* after its simple, some might say repetitive 4/4 time measure. What about a manuscript called *four to the floor* where the book's form becomes a machine according to fours?

Disco makes you dance. Disco removes your body from the instrumental world placing your limbs in a possibility of the open moment. But before you arrive at the club you've been thinking all day long, or at least from noon to six. Then there is the pre-game where we tell each other stories from six to midnight. Now, the club where two records mix into eight syllables. At six in the morning the clubs close so your stuck in the afterglow of sunrise. There you have it: a day divided by fours programmed around the machine of disco.

I See Disco Everywhere I Look

What is it that/gives a face
to/things
in a rest/aurant?

—frozen/adjunct limit/less terrific

                                    it does not pro/duce abstraction

because it does/remind
one of/being
in an/other eater/y

                              in anoth/er time

not al/together sep/arate
from this/one where the chair/is

                          or was

hold/ing its self up
through sheer presence
of oak..

There is/also a bod/y who sat there
or sits, which a/gain reminds
by/its elbowness/& brick

                          of limb

& overall/axis of the/utensils
han/dling the food
from the plates pres/entation to/the infinite
        problems
afford/ed the mouth.

The/fact is that de/sire produces/reality. The fork's tip un/done
brings it to/the tilt.

It. It/It, It, It,

a/word that hardly/makes sense
even/ in a restaur/ant even though/it is

                                    just a/little bit vow/el

              a brittle/stroke through the beard

                          in contempla/tion.

The Problem of Remembering Phil if Remembering is Going to be Disco

Like a future story told around the early party evening we drove to the west end of Galveston Island. Oh yeah, the hurricane-dead were plenty. Scenic enough for a little picnic number. No, no, not the dead, *at least not now* (which is to say memory of then), but the mild feast we were already fidgeting with. Seated on the car's hood you (being the reader if you went, which is what we're trying to establish) could see (or can) the continental US of A dolled up in smokestacks. What Phil had to say (or has) *depending on how close you've been following,* will become important, but please a moment to accept time. It's longer than you'd ((everyone) *ever)* think, the distance from wrist to elbow or the vast increment within which the tongue has room. Hack a year from the end of my life (not now) *this was then,(being made presently),* if I can fish like the pelican, hell fly like would be enough, *but enough Phil wants us to come upstairs.* He teaches Lit. to high school punks in the Houston suburbs. He's not sweating it. He's already made his fortune designing tests to separate the men from the boys, Englishly at least, and the women from the girls, in other words the slick talkers from the I don't knows—all in the state of bull and hydrocarbons. How can you argue (I'm with you on this one reader) with a man who drives an hour and a half each way to toast himself to this seclusion. Legally no one can build a house between Phil and the bay. And there was quite literally a ninth inning whisper whispering from Phil's hand radio. (I suppose this is a road trip's hope, the manifestation of humanity because it's not a roommate.) Whatever Phil wanted from us was *or is* serious stuff because he wanted *or wants* it with his shirt off and toes fully liberated. *My god Phil, you* (just Phil this time) *didn't change our lives* (although the reader can speak for itself), *but that's neither here nor there.* What I'd like to know then *as much as now* is how a man can stoke the fire between his spleen and the verbs on his knuckles? Rumor has it we're (sure reader, you're welcome too) going to visit Phil's spread again. I guess it's just something you say when you leave.

The Disco of Miles Davis

there is no black
with history's
depth—back of neck
imp's teeth chatter

a Lazarus
smile—in part his
muscle tone groans
like construction

enjoy foreheads
tonight with
dreams of toenails
enough
pushing, curling

evidence that we have not yet
      mastered the language—stomach
of thick meals toss germ heat across

until ripe sheets wad in relief

Hungarian pocked
is difficult
just cool

to trust bridges

nose churn the skin
these hell bucket's
of rotten gold
impossible

sleep wheelied through
eastern europe
my cheeks are numb
with horse hair braid

Four Disco Negative's

1.

As perfect a day in the suburbs as the faithful could ask, almost a pillow case. The television has what's on: Saturday and Lithuania remains undefeated. Though the hangovers refuse there are flight patterns where clouds daunt the klaxons. How can we arrive? Where is that impossible forensic detail? Would anyone out there like a bite of this wild body language? A dance hall is a dance hall is a dance hall of sleep filled urgency?

2.

The neighbor has been moving rocks this whole time. The grand toilets waiting in safety for the day to let. One man makes a basket, another misses, yet another claps in the distance. There is no crime to any of it. There is no grip on advertisement. To the kids peanut butter and jelly sounds like August.

3.

And where we go from here is like asking several people to wait in line without air conditioning. Would the accordion player recognize the tune? What accordion player and what tadpoles vying for the Budapest polka? I'm sorry but I'm just back from Europe and they don't like songs on the subway either.

4.

Perhaps the great lesson is this such and such perspective on so and so: they were never meant to be liked. So, the intrinsic walk down Alameda Boulevard where poker games fire blanks. What the hell is to be done with these husbands and wives? All of their fucking brunch in the automobile's whir.

Four
To
The
Floor.

INSTITUTE FOR THE BUILT ENVIRONMENT AT COLORADO STATE UNIVERSITY - PROVIDING RESOURCES FOR DESIGN PROFESSIONALS

Local Designs

Local Projects

Integrated Team

Integrated Design

ARCHITECTURE WEST, L.L.C.
ARCHITECTURE/PLANNING

bha

BHA DESIGN INCORPORATED

SunJuice
Integrated Solar Design

THE BRENDLE GROUP, INC.

KECHTER ROAD

Real Dirt
Garden Design

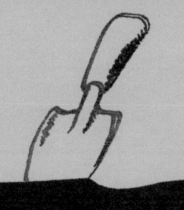

Constance Zybko
Landscape Architect

970 498 0649

ED HAIMES CONSTRUCTION

SPECIALIZING IN STRAW BALE HOMES
FOR OVER 30 YEARS
HOME: 970.278.0662
CELL: 970.231.1384

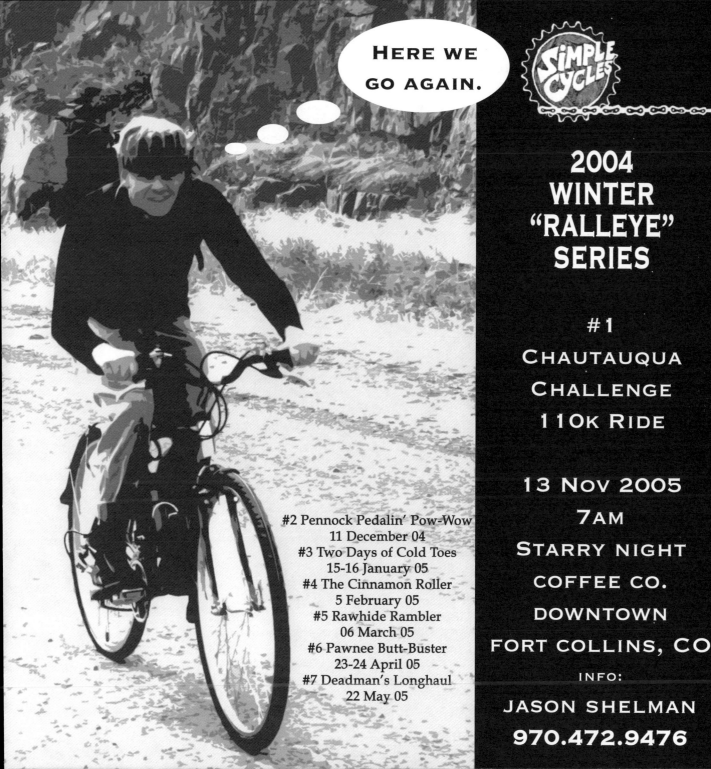

Cafe Ardour

powered by wind.

Ardour 1 a: an often restless or tansitory warmth of feeling <the sudden ardours of youth> **b:** extreme vigor or energy: INTENSITY **c:** ZEAL **d:** LOYALTY

225 Linden St.
Fort Collins
M-W: 7:30 am - 6 pm
Th-Sat: 7:30 am - 9 pm
Sunday 10 am - 5 pm

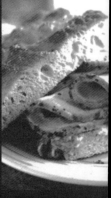

Serving impeccable espresso, salads, panini, and baked goods made with fresh, local, organic indredients

live music on friday evenings - local art

we appreciate support.

custom 29er's, singlespeeds, fixies, and commuter good

BRAVE
NEW WHEEL

105 East Myrtle   Fort Collins, CO   970.416.04

"I still feel that variable gears are only for people over forty-five. Isn't it better to triumph by the strength of your muscles than by the artifice of a derailer? We are getting soft... As for me, give me a fixed gear!"
-Henri Desgrange

Concerned About Colorado's Forests?

Colorado is blessed with 14.4 million acres of spectacular national forests. Yet they are threatened by the Bush administration's so called "Healthy Forests Initiative". While many fuels reduction projects may help protect homes from forest fire, others are simply logging under the guise of fuels reduction.

Preserving our forest heritage takes work. Colorado Wild has been an effective, efficient, and realistic advocate for forest conservation since 1998.

We Cover the State

In Your Backyard

Colorado Wild works to preserve the clean water, recreation, and natural resources that Colorado's seven national forests provide. Alongside scientists, land managers, communities, and all of us that hunt, bike, fish, and hike, we strive to ensure that the Forest Service makes informed management decisions so that coming generations have what each and every one of us loves of our national forests.

Near Redfeather Lakes west of Ft. Collins, we're challenging the Forest Service to improve their approach to fire protection. We're asking the tough questions and demanding honest answers. Are clearcuts necessary to protect homes? Can the risk to residents be reduced without harming the forests we love? Our fundamental premise: scientifically informed, cautious decisions benefit both people and the forests.

You Can Help! Learn more:

www.coloradowild.org

Online you can join our newsletter mailing list, or become a member.
Alternately, call us at 303-839-5900, or write to P.O. Box 2434, Durango, CO 81302.

Nature's Own

201 Linden St.
Ft. Collins, CO 80524
970.484.9701

HEARNE'S

old town square
fort collins
970.224.4653

e comfort shoe place"

leather goods.

art-to-wear
atural fiber clothing

rocky mountain
BULLHORN
News, Views & Culture of Northern Colorado

Review

FRONT RANGE

Front Range Review, the literary magazine published by the Creative Writing Program at Front Range Community College, seeks quality short fiction, poetry, and creative nonfiction for its fifth annual issue. Our reading period is August 15 - December 1 each year. Send your best work to:

Blair Oliver, Faculty Advisor
Front Range Review, FRCC,
4616 S. Shields, FT. Collins, CO 80526.

Why **plant trees?**

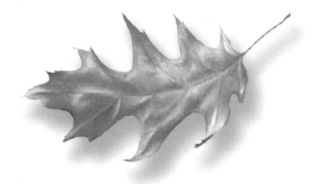

Healthy forests are ***not*** a luxury; they are vital to the overall health of our planet. Trees help control erosion and protect water supplies, and forests are important reservoirs of biodiversity and play a critical role in regulating the global climate.

Each of us uses an average of approximately 65 cubic feet of wood every year – equivalent to **six** 12-14" diameter trees – in paper and wood products. Worldwide, tree harvesting outstrips replanting by a ratio of 10:1, threatening the clean water, clear air, and livelihoods of many people.

How can ***you*** help? You can replant the trees you use, quickly and easily, by joining the **100% Replanted program**.

To find out more, visit **www.replanttrees.org**.

100% REPLANTED

REDUCE - REUSE - RECYCLE - *REPLANT*

A project of Trees, Water & People and Your True Nature, Inc

www.leescyclery.com

WORLD RENOWNED BREWING EFFICIENCY

ON-SITE PROCESS WATER TREATMENT

ALTERNATIVE LIGHT SOURCES

RENEWABLE HEATING AND COOLING SYSTEMS

98% WASTE STREAM DIVERSION RATE

ORGANIC WEARABLES

UNDER 5:1 WATER USE RATIO

CO-GENERATION

WIND POWER

N   E   W   B

WORLD RENOWNED BREWING EFFICIENCY

ON-SITE PROCESS WATER TREATMENT

ALTERNATIVE LIGHT SOURCES

RENEWABLE HEATING AND COOLING SYSTEMS

98% WASTE STREAM DIVERSION RATE

ORGANIC WEARABLES

UNDER 5:1 WATER USE RATIO

CO-GENERATION

WIND POWER

L   G   I   U   M

revolve

lifeonabike.tripod.com

Fort Collins Food Co-Op

205 E. Mountain Ave · 970.484.7448

Locally Grown since 1972!

CYCLOGROPHIES

Genevieve Betts is currently working on her MFA in creative writing at Arizona State University, publishing poetry and reviews in *42opus, The G-Spot,* and *LEGACY.* She lugged her cheap beach cruiser through Europe for one and a half months, where many people squeezed its tires and seat when they thought she was not looking.

Jacob Burd lives with his wife and cat. He is currently working on a long poem.

The first bike **Steven Church** ever loved was a yellow Schwinn Scrambler with a banana seat. He still rides a yellow Schwinn—but it's all fancy aluminum and stuff. The last bike he will love belonged to his father. It's a red 1953 Western Flyer with the original white-wall Firestone tires, a chrome accented gas tank, and battery operated horn. He keeps it in his garage for now, but hopes to hang it on the wall someday. Yes, he knows it's probably worth some money on EBay. But that's not really important, is it? Steven has published things in places. He's been nominated for more awards than he's actually won. His first book, *The Guinness Book of Me: a Memoir of Record*, will be published in 2005 by Simon and Schuster.

Carol Deering is currently director of library services at Central Wyoming College. She has ridden bicycles and has been a passenger on motorcycles, and in trains, buses, cars, and trucks—but probably the wheels which had the most impact on her life were part of the landing gear when she flew from New England to live in the West.

The extraordinary power of the ordinary bicycle was first revealed to **Sue Ring deRosset** during the 1970s gas crisis in Brussels, Belgium. On Sundays—when the citizens of Brussels were prohibited from driving—she and her sister were permitted to ride their small bicycles up and down the quiet cobblestone streets. Today, Sue bike-commutes to Front Range Community College, where she teaches in the Veterinary Technology Program. She lives in downtown Fort Collins with two fine dogs, three soft cats, a rambunctious herd of bicycles, and a loving, bike-wacko husband.

William deRosset lives in inner-city Fort Collins with his wife, Susan, two dogs, three cats and seven bicycles. He is a foster rider for Vélocipede Rescue, a non-profit organization that provides emergency support, herd housing, maintenance, and regular exercise for neglected exotic bicycles.

Derek Esposito is a graduate student in Sustainable Building at Colorado State University. His graduate work revolves around research done with the Biomimicry Guild linking biology and architecture. He received his undergraduate degree in Vermont, incidentally, the same place where he acquired his vintage-era red K2 Proflex mountain bike which has now been converted into the ultimate cruising machine. When not teaching in the backcountry classroom with the National Outdoor Leadership School, Derek can be spotted on his full-suspension cruiser about Old Town, contemplating timeless questions such as "the origin of irreducible complexity" and "where to get a pint."

Trevor Even is a young, friendly human who was once told to take several hundred dollars worth of pills per month to suppress aberrant aspects of his personality. He recently just exited a period of his life where he did not sleep at night, and did not dream, and worked as a Chinese food delivery driver. He wrote on his lunch breaks.

David Gruber hasn't ridden a bicycle since the first Bush administration, but sometimes thinks that he could use the exercise. He has lived in Florida, New York, Pennsylvania, New Hampshire, Colorado, and now in Tennessee, all places where you should really have a bike helmet.

Derrick Jensen is the author of many books and CDs, including *A Language Older Than Words* and *The Culture of Make Believe*. The excerpt included in this issue is from his book *What Goes Up....*, scheduled for release in the fall of 2005. More information is available at his website: www.derrickjensen.org

Kendra Kellogg says, "When I was an eight year old, I had a pair of roller skates stuck to my feet at all times. In my Littleton neighborhood they paved a new parking lot, and compared to my eight year old frame, it was an endless expanse of asphalt from horizon to horizon. I fell in love. Nowadays, I have oil paint stuck to me at all times. I am an artist here in Fort Collins, working towards an MFA."

Keith Kimmel is a visionary and a recluse except when he's socializing or in Vegas. His published work can be found in bookstores across the country. Discover his frequently updated website, KeithKimmel.net, where he's currently working on his second novel, *Why Pigeons Don't Fly Too Much*. He does not own a bicycle.

Brian Kiteley has published two novels, *Still Life with Insects* and *I Know Many Songs, But I Cannot Sing*. A book of his fiction exercises, *A Writers Book of Matches*, will be published in 2005 by Writers Digest

Press. He has received Guggenheim, Whiting, and NEA fellowships. Brian Kiteley directs the creative writing program at the University of Denver.

Joan Marsan rode around the block on her brother and sister's hand-me-down little red bike. Now she lives in Laramie and pedals a little farther, and her bike is blue.

Heather Martin is a New York transplant working toward a Ph.D. at the University of Denver. She moved here by way of Brooklyn and has been suffering from "good pizza" withdrawal ever since. Pizza aside, Denver is a great city—especially for biking. Coasting through Wash Park often takes her back to the days of her suburban girlhood. Biking was the ultimate freedom, zooming through the circular mazes of generic cookie-cutter houses organized into cul-de-sacs and quads. From behind the handlebars, she learned about life, love, and lawn ornaments. Her work recently appeared in *Coffee Press Journal* and is forthcoming in *Electric Velocipede*.

Laura Mullen is the author of four books of poetry, the most recent of which, *Subject* is forthcoming from University of California Press. She is on the faculty at Louisiana State University (Baton Rouge), where she teaches bicycle riding and manufacture, basing her instruction on a certain "ready made" assembled by Marcel Duchamp....

Jefferson Navicky lives in Boulder, CO where he rides his cream-colored Kronan cruiser, named Betty, all over town. Betty has a great rack above her back tire and a generator light, which is, Jefferson thinks, the coolest thing. She is named after his great aunt who could smoke and drink with the best of them.

Gary Norris lives, writes, and teaches in Denver where two of his bikes have been stolen, only one recovered. In 1977 his was given his first bike: a Schwinn Stingray, sparkling red, with a banana seat. Extremely proud, he rode it well past his bedtime round and round his block. He cruised down one side of the block arms folded across his chest, no hands. He raced up the other side in what he still recalls one swift pedal towards—he has moved so to ever since.

Patrick Odenbeck rides a bike he calls the Golden Ratio. Patrick this is us making it up to you for forgetting your name last issue. Remember, his name is Odenbeck.

Blair Oliver's work has appeared in *Red Rock Review, Yale Anglers' Journal, Iron Horse Literary Review, CutBank, Talking River Review, Dickinson Review,* and elsewhere. He teaches creative writing and literature at Front Range Community College here in Fort Collins, where he's also the founding editor of *Front Range Review*, a national literary magazine. His outdoor writing appears in a regular column in *Yellowstone Journal*. His haunting fear is that he'll spend middle age riding a too-small bicycle with a six-pack in the basket, ringing the bell.

Alex Paozols rides a refurbished Bridgestone Bub with mustache handlebars that he inherited from his former neighbor, Damien. He would like to cook for you. He can be contacted at alexpaozols@yahoo.com.

Claire Petersky learned how to ride a bike when she was six, and she has had an an-ongoing meditation practice for about 25 years. Her website on the practice of bicycling meditation may be found at: http://home.earthlink.net/~cpetersky/Welcome.htm

Bin Ramke says, "When I was growing up I had a horse, but did have a bicycle, too. I preferred the horse. I thought I was going to be a mathematician, but ended up writing poems. I am not sure whether I prefer poems or proofs, but I suppose I am better at the poems. My most recent book is called **MATTER**."

Morgan Reitmeyer lay half in the street, her head inches from the ground, heart pumping burgundy onto the slick sidewalk. The paper which had been cradled in her right arm was fluttering along the Durango Mesa, animal wild twisting in the early spring wind. The bike looked at her innocently, one wheel spinning gently, calmly. She took a breath in to curse, but released it with a sigh. The bike, green and old and heavy, grinned somehow. She was in the moment.

Matt Roberts rides his sleek black cruiser with the blood-red rims and chrome fangs in Tempe, Arizona these days. "Blackula," like any good steed, doesn't complain about the heat.

Wayne Sheldrake has entered the Mt. Evans Hillclimb for Velo News, Mt. Gazette, and Outdoor Explorer. He is the last cyclist to ride from Alamosa to Denver via 285 and live.

Ian Tyson says, "Born and raised in Alaska where my fifth birthday was the occasion for my first bike. Immediately I took the present off a jump far too big, a jump I had been warned against, and split my knee open. Grounded for the next week by my parents I could only imagine myself riding the bike again. I had to pretend. Since then my pretending has led me to a boarding school in Minnesota then onto to West Point where my pretending gave me the boot. That's why I prefer the CSU MFA program, they let me pretend."

Robert Urquhart spent the years from age thirteen to age seventeen on a bicycle, riding around West Sussex with his best friend. Now, he teaches economics at University of Denver.

Clotilde Wright is currently pursuing her MFA in Writing and Poetics at Naropa University. In her free time she contemplates the nature of existence.

I hit **the wall**, unable to ride. I am alone in the dark, again, on the eastern border of Boulder County. The clouds that have been gathering, then descending, finally fall open and begin to **rain on me**. I eat all the food I have left, drink two water bottles, clamber **back onto the bike**, and limp **to the finish** at half-speed. A fellow in a truck stops at the **edge of the sprawl** and asks if I need help. I pedal on, through empty suburban streets, and finally arrive about 45 minutes later than my pickup time, two hours and forty-five minutes outside my **"easily achievable"** time.